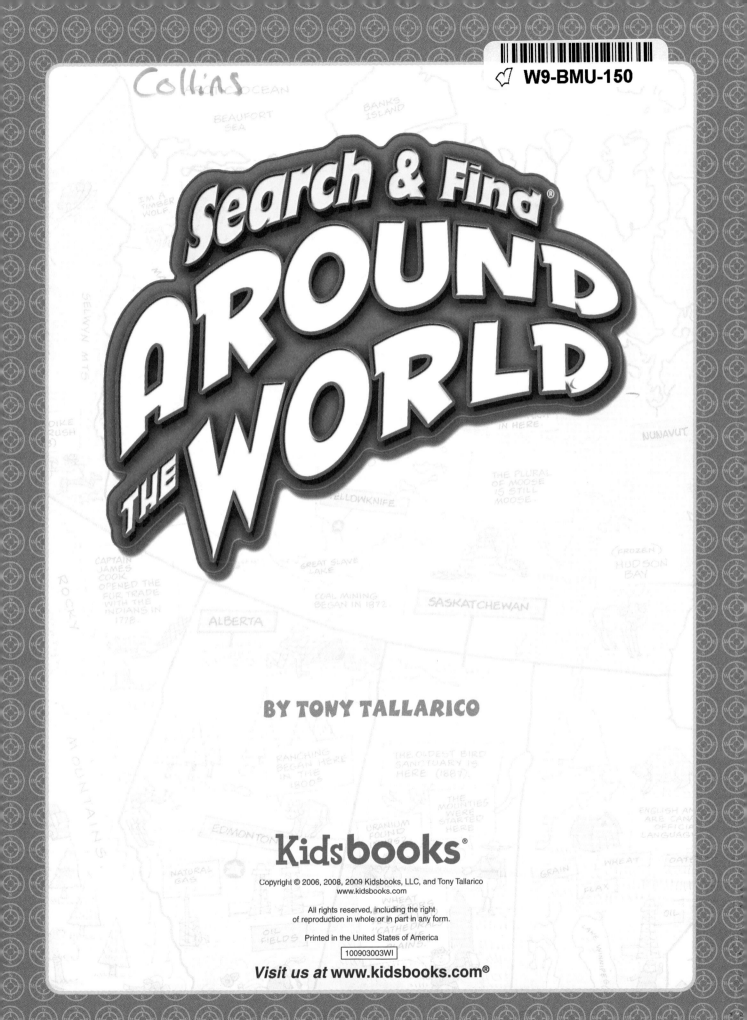

Search & Find® AROUND THE WORLD

BY TONY TALLARICO

Collins

ASIA, AUSTRALIA, AND OCEANIA

Asia, the largest of the continents, stretches from above the Arctic Circle to below the equator, and from the Ural Mountains in the west to the Pacific Ocean in the east. Asia's lands include some of the coldest, hottest, wettest, and driest places on Earth.

South and east of Asia lie Australia, New Zealand, and many small island nations in the Pacific, most of which lie south of the equator. Together, they form a region that is known as Oceania.

LEARN ABOUT ASIA, AUSTRALIA, AND OCEANIA AS YOU LOOK FOR THESE FUN ITEMS:

- ❏ Birds (2)
- ❏ Coffeepot
- ❏ Elephant
- ❏ Gold
- ❏ Kangaroo
- ❏ Lobster
- ❏ Mermaid
- ❏ Mountain climber
- ❏ Octopus
- ❏ Oil well
- ❏ Penguin
- ❏ Polar bear
- ❏ Telescope
- ❏ Windsurfer

4

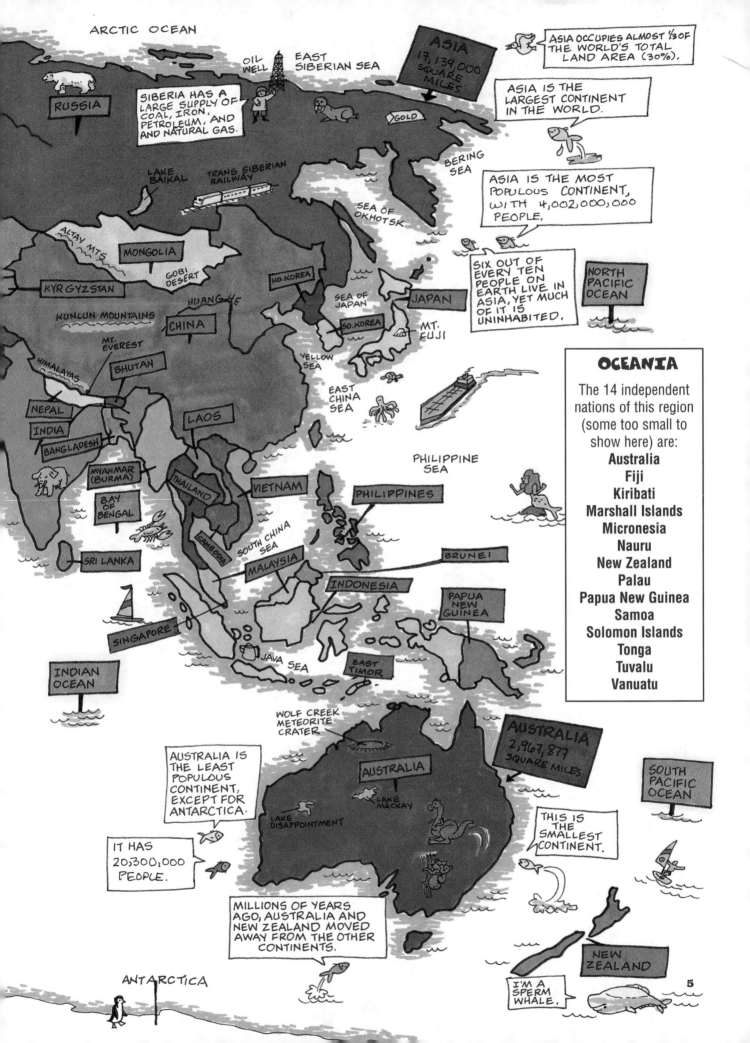

RUSSIA TAKES UP ONE SEVENTH OF THE WORLD'S TOTAL LAND AREA AND HAS THE EIGHTH LARGEST POPULATION.

TWO-THIRDS OF RUSSIA'S POPULATION LIVES IN EUROPE, WHILE ONLY A THIRD LIVES IN ASIA.

SNOW COVERS MORE THAN HALF OF RUSSIA FOR SIX MONTHS OF THE YEAR.

KARA SEA

BARENTS SEA

RUSSIA

FORESTS COVER MORE THAN HALF THE COUNTRY.

WHITE SEA

CARS AND TRACTORS MANUFACTURING

URAL MTS.

THE URAL MTS. DIVIDE RUSSIA BETWEEN EUROPE AND ASIA.

YENISEY RIVER

LAKE ONEGA

BALTIC SEA

LAKE LADOGA

ST. BASIL'S CATHEDRAL

GULF OF FINLAND

POTATOES

WHEAT

MOSCOW

BOLSHOI BALLET

OUR POPULATION IS 15,200,000.

OUR LANGUAGES ARE KAZAKH AND RUSSIAN.

WE ARE ALMOST TWICE THE SIZE OF ALASKA.

THE REGION THAT LIES BETWEEN THE BLACK SEA AND THE CASPIAN SEA IS CALLED THE CAUCASUS.

OUR COUNTRY IS MAINLY STEPPE (A VAST SEMI-ARID PLAIN), DESERT, AND MOUNTAIN.

KAZAKHSTAN

ALTAY MTS

GEORGIA'S POPULATION IS 4,650,000.

THE MAIN SPACE CENTER FOR THE COMMONWEALTH IS LOCATED HERE.

ASTANA

95% OF OUR COUNTRY IS MOUNTAINOUS.

ITS WARM CLIMATE ATTRACTS TOURISTS.

ITS LANGUAGES ARE GEORGIAN, RUSSIAN, ARMENIAN, AND AZERI.

TBILISI

OIL

UZBEKISTAN

TASHKENT

BISHKEK

BLACK SEA

CASPIAN SEA

KYRGYZSTAN

ASHGABAT

COMMUNISM PEAK (24,590 FT)

GEORGIA

BAKU

90% IS COVERED BY KARA-KUM DESERT.

TAJIKISTAN

OUR POPULATION IS 7,300,000, AND OUR LANGUAGE IS TAJIK (ALSO RUSSIAN).

ARMENIA

AZERBAIJAN

YEREVAN

TURKMENISTAN

MEDITERRANEAN SEA

DUSHANBE

THE LANGUAGES OF AZERBAIJAN ARE AZERI, RUSSIAN, AND ARMENIAN.

THEIR POPULATION IS 8,200,000.

ARMENIA IS THE MOST INDUSTRIALIZED STATE IN THE CAUCASUS.

ITS POPULATION IS 3,000,000.

TURKMENISTAN'S POPULATION IS 5,200,000, AND ITS LANGUAGES ARE TURKMEN, RUSSIAN, AND UZBEK.

MAIN LANGUAGES SPOKEN ARE ARMENIAN AND RUSSIAN.

RUSSIA AND ITS NEIGHBORS

Russia, the world's largest country, spans two continents. It covers more than 50 percent of Europe and more than 35 percent of Asia.

Russia used to be part of an even bigger nation called the Soviet Union, which broke apart in 1991. Many of the countries to Russia's south, now independent, also were part of the Soviet Union until 1991.

EUROPE

ASIA

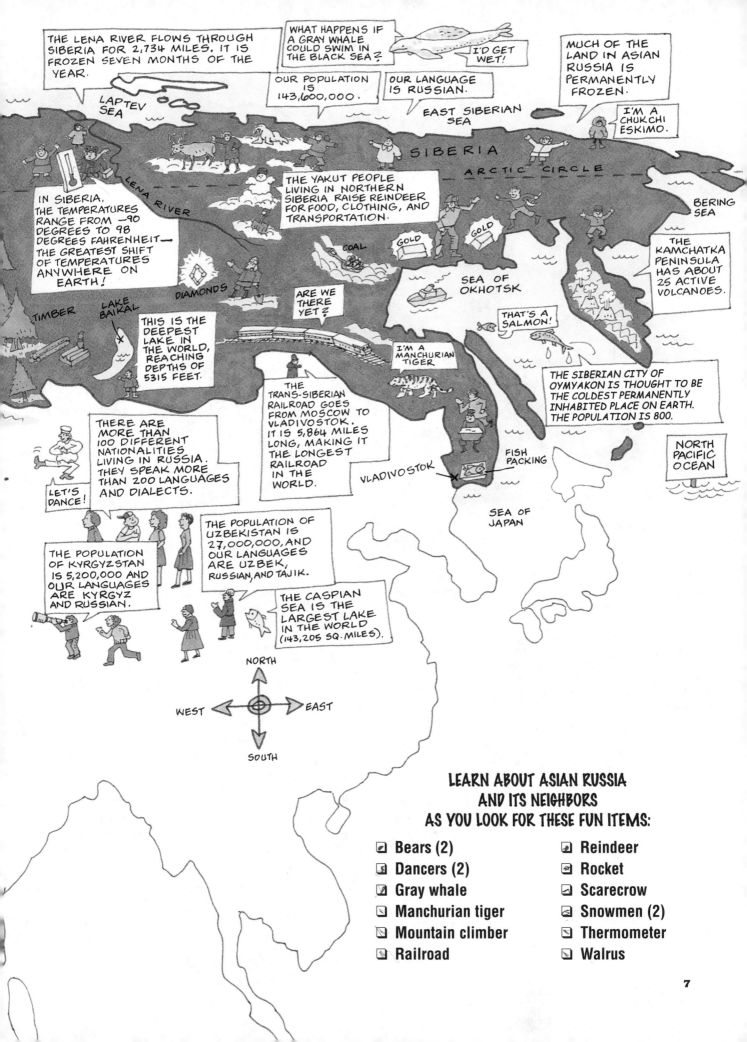

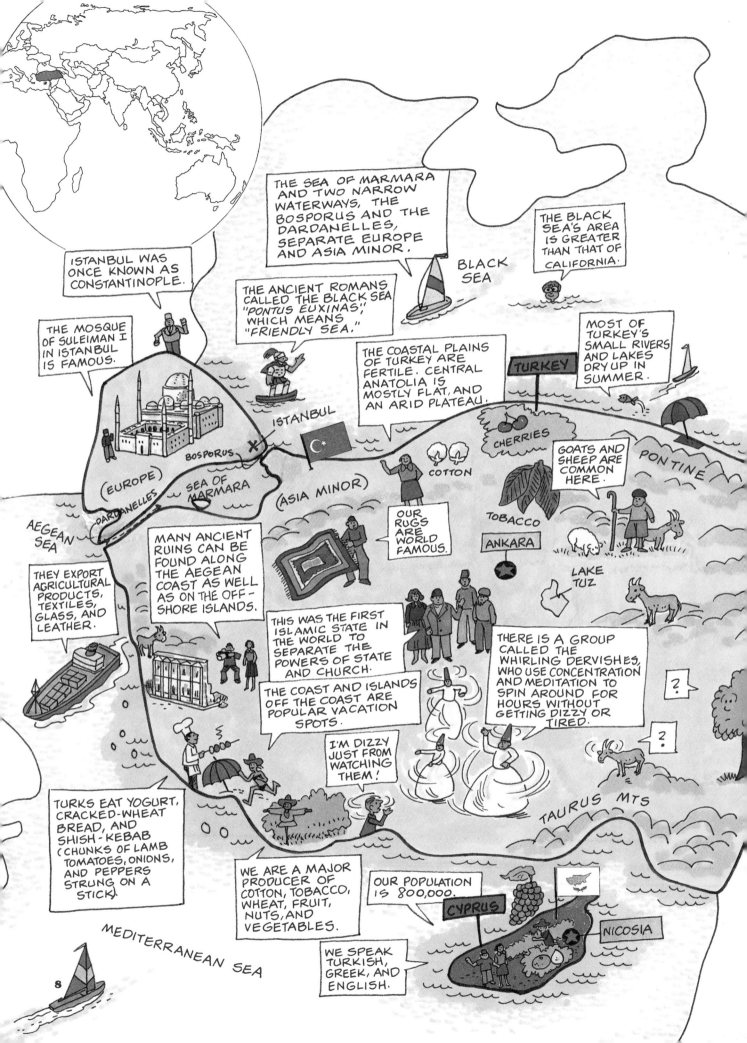

TURKEY AND CYPRUS

Three percent of Turkey's land area lies in Europe. The rest is in Asia, in a region known as Anatolia or Asia Minor. Istanbul, which is Turkey's largest city, is the only city in the world that occupies land on two continents.

Cyprus is only 140 miles long at its longest point, and 60 miles wide at its widest point. It has long been controlled by other nations, and Greece and Turkey both still claim parts of it.

LEARN ABOUT TURKEY AND CYPRUS AS YOU LOOK FOR THESE FUN ITEMS:

- ❏ Apples
- ❏ Ball
- ❏ Bears (3)
- ❏ Book
- ❏ Cook
- ❏ Cowboy
- ❏ Egg
- ❏ Fish
- ❏ Goats (5)
- ❏ Grapes
- ❏ Ibis
- ❏ Ladder
- ❏ Sailboats (3)
- ❏ Shepherd
- ❏ Tea bag
- ❏ Telescope
- ❏ Tin man
- ❏ Umbrellas (2)

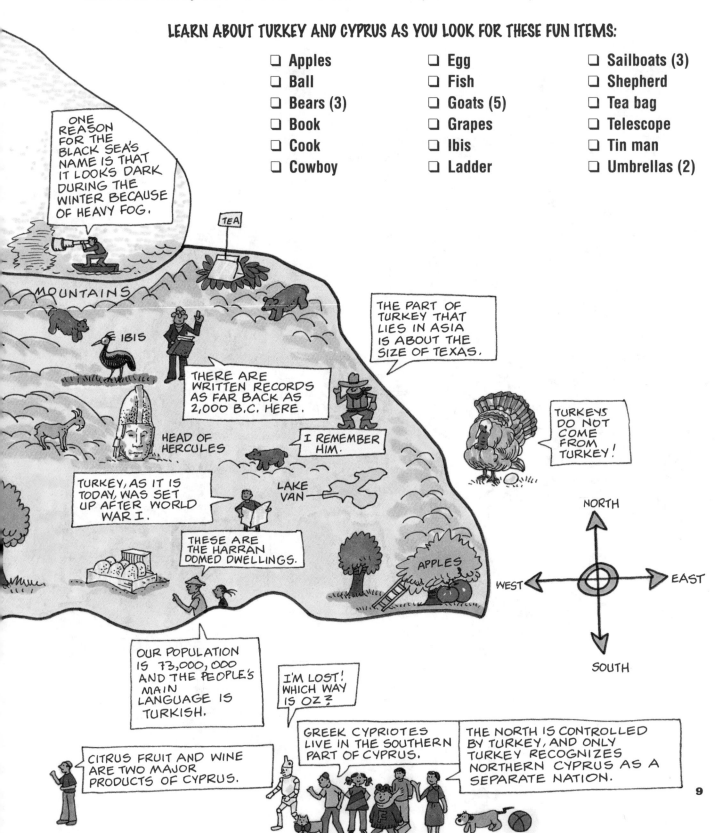

THE MIDDLE EAST

This part of Asia, in the area between the Tigris and Euphrates rivers, was one of the first places where civilization was recorded. Towns and communities were thriving here 6,000 years ago. The Arabian Peninsula *(see pp. 12-13)* is also part of the Middle East—a region that has about 75 percent of the world's oil reserves.

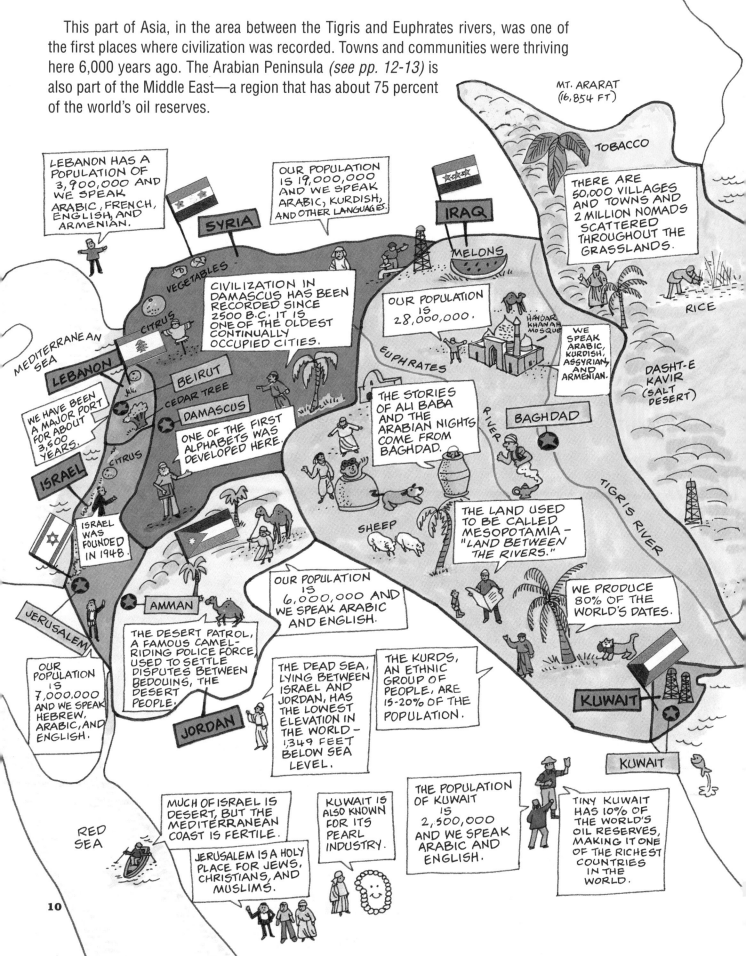

MT. ARARAT (16,854 FT)

TOBACCO

LEBANON HAS A POPULATION OF 3,900,000 AND WE SPEAK ARABIC, FRENCH, ENGLISH, AND ARMENIAN.

OUR POPULATION IS 19,000,000 AND WE SPEAK ARABIC, KURDISH, AND OTHER LANGUAGES.

SYRIA

IRAQ

THERE ARE 50,000 VILLAGES AND TOWNS AND 2 MILLION NOMADS SCATTERED THROUGHOUT THE GRASSLANDS.

MELONS

VEGETABLES

CIVILIZATION IN DAMASCUS HAS BEEN RECORDED SINCE 2500 B.C. IT IS ONE OF THE OLDEST CONTINUALLY OCCUPIED CITIES.

OUR POPULATION IS 28,000,000.

HAIDAR KHANAH MOSQUE

RICE

CITRUS

MEDITERRANEAN SEA

EUPHRATES

WE SPEAK ARABIC, KURDISH, ASSYRIAN, AND ARMENIAN.

DASHT-E KAVIR (SALT DESERT)

LEBANON

BEIRUT

CEDAR TREE

DAMASCUS

THE STORIES OF ALI BABA AND THE ARABIAN NIGHTS COME FROM BAGHDAD.

BAGHDAD

RIVER

WE HAVE BEEN A MAJOR PORT FOR ABOUT 3,500 YEARS.

ONE OF THE FIRST ALPHABETS WAS DEVELOPED HERE.

CITRUS

ISRAEL

ISRAEL WAS FOUNDED IN 1948.

THE LAND USED TO BE CALLED MESOPOTAMIA – "LAND BETWEEN THE RIVERS."

TIGRIS RIVER

SHEEP

WE PRODUCE 80% OF THE WORLD'S DATES.

AMMAN

OUR POPULATION IS 6,000,000 AND WE SPEAK ARABIC AND ENGLISH.

JERUSALEM

OUR POPULATION IS 7,000,000 AND WE SPEAK HEBREW, ARABIC, AND ENGLISH.

THE DESERT PATROL, A FAMOUS CAMEL-RIDING POLICE FORCE, USED TO SETTLE DISPUTES BETWEEN BEDOUINS, THE DESERT PEOPLE.

THE DEAD SEA, LYING BETWEEN ISRAEL AND JORDAN, HAS THE LOWEST ELEVATION IN THE WORLD – 1,349 FEET BELOW SEA LEVEL.

THE KURDS, AN ETHNIC GROUP OF PEOPLE, ARE 15-20% OF THE POPULATION.

KUWAIT

JORDAN

KUWAIT

RED SEA

MUCH OF ISRAEL IS DESERT, BUT THE MEDITERRANEAN COAST IS FERTILE.

KUWAIT IS ALSO KNOWN FOR ITS PEARL INDUSTRY.

THE POPULATION OF KUWAIT IS 2,500,000 AND WE SPEAK ARABIC AND ENGLISH.

TINY KUWAIT HAS 10% OF THE WORLD'S OIL RESERVES, MAKING IT ONE OF THE RICHEST COUNTRIES IN THE WORLD.

JERUSALEM IS A HOLY PLACE FOR JEWS, CHRISTIANS, AND MUSLIMS.

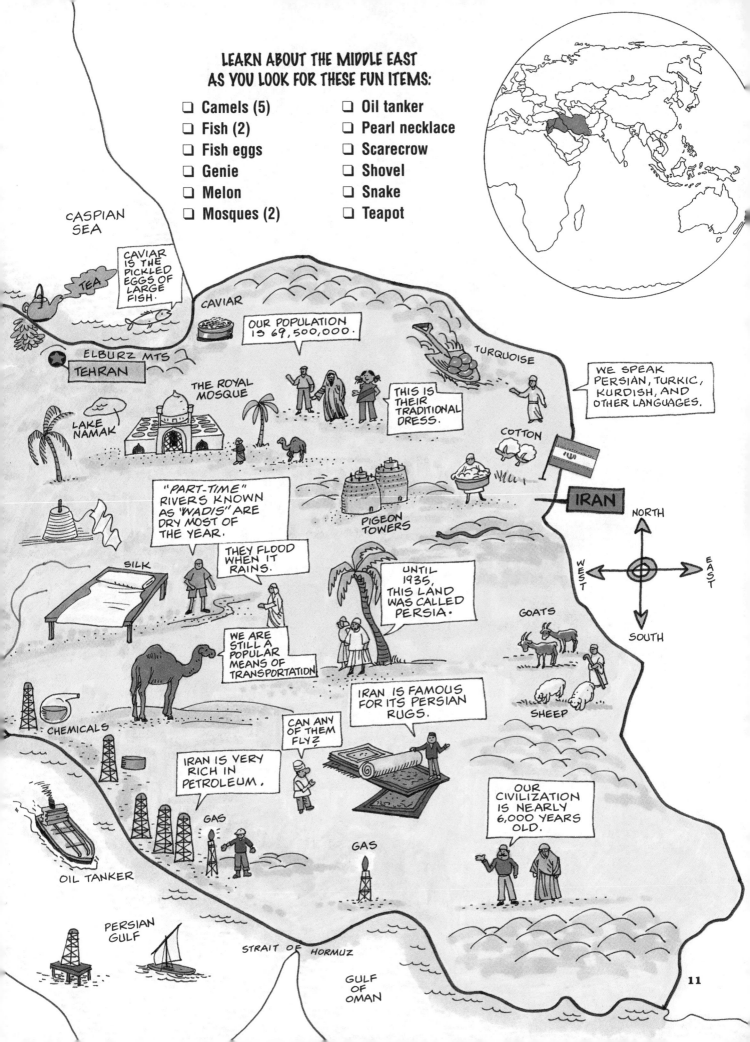

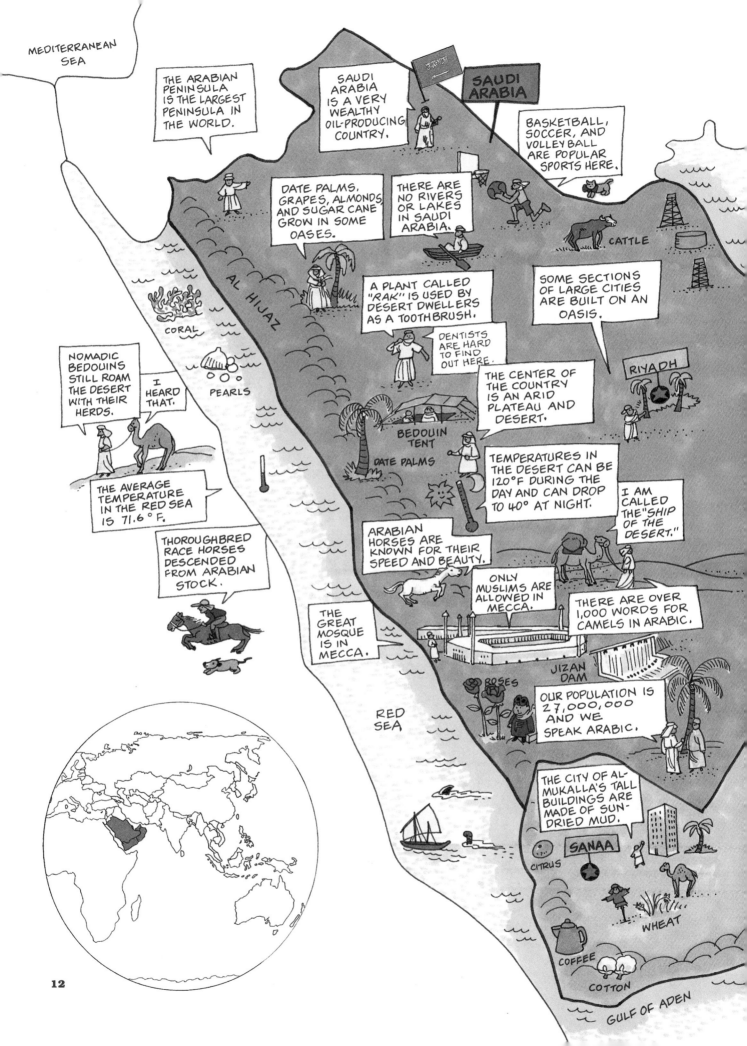

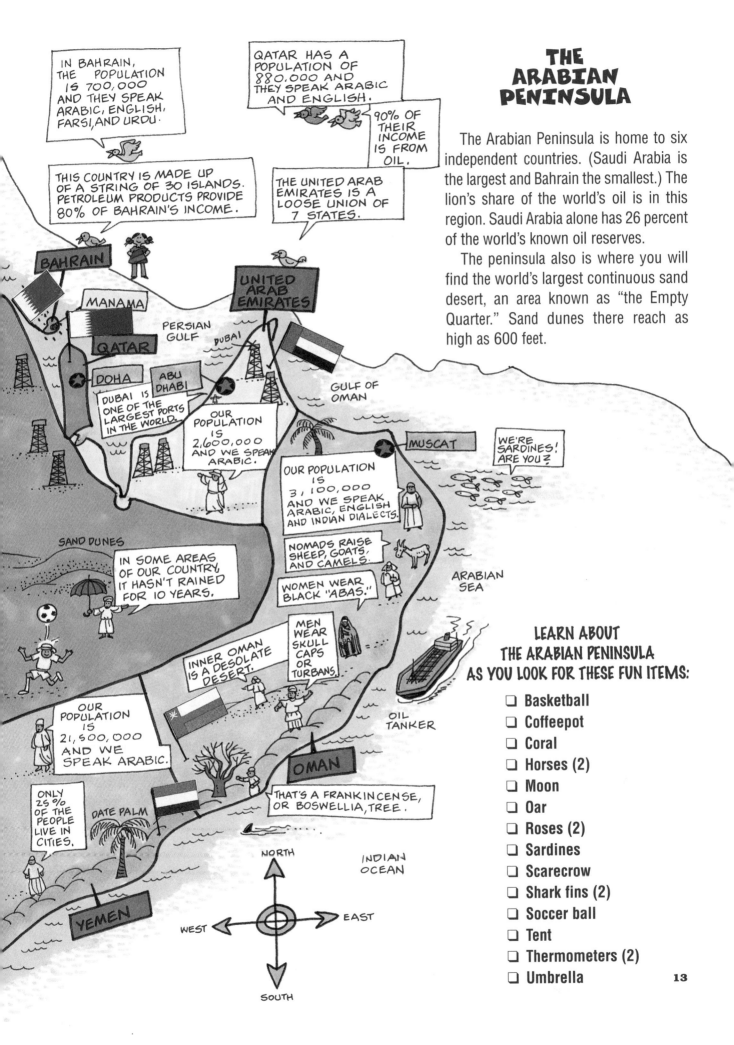

THE ARABIAN PENINSULA

The Arabian Peninsula is home to six independent countries. (Saudi Arabia is the largest and Bahrain the smallest.) The lion's share of the world's oil is in this region. Saudi Arabia alone has 26 percent of the world's known oil reserves.

The peninsula also is where you will find the world's largest continuous sand desert, an area known as "the Empty Quarter." Sand dunes there reach as high as 600 feet.

LEARN ABOUT THE ARABIAN PENINSULA AS YOU LOOK FOR THESE FUN ITEMS:

- ❏ Basketball
- ❏ Coffeepot
- ❏ Coral
- ❏ Horses (2)
- ❏ Moon
- ❏ Oar
- ❏ Roses (2)
- ❏ Sardines
- ❏ Scarecrow
- ❏ Shark fins (2)
- ❏ Soccer ball
- ❏ Tent
- ❏ Thermometers (2)
- ❏ Umbrella

13

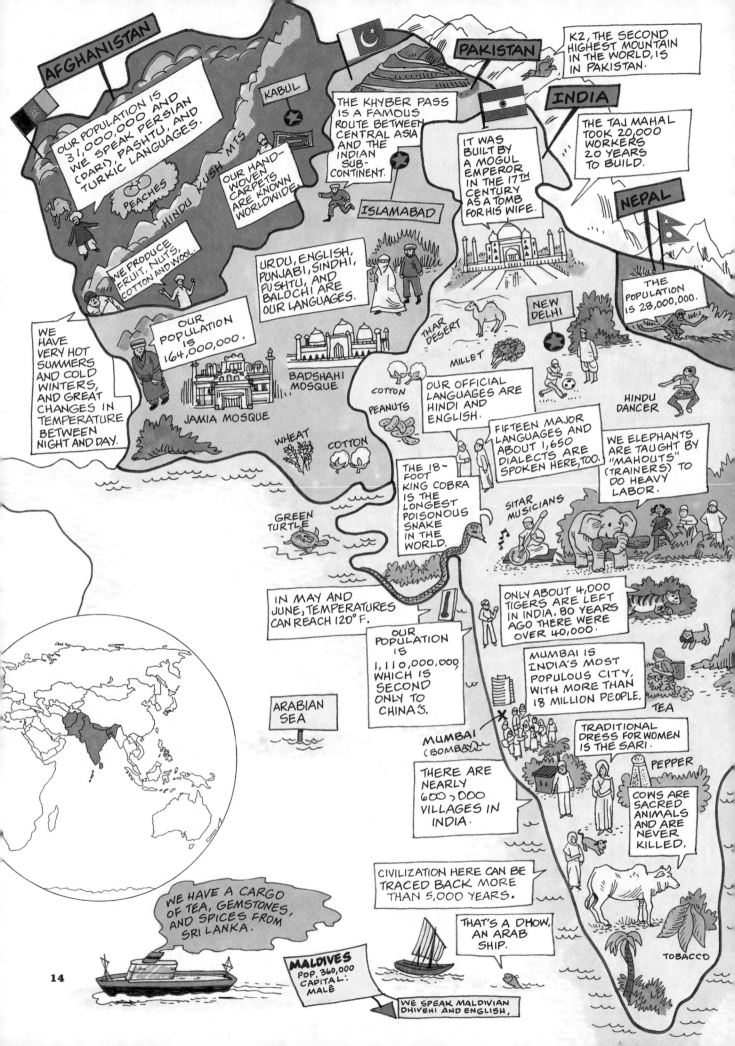

AFGHANISTAN

OUR POPULATION IS 31,000,000 AND WE SPEAK PERSIAN (DARI), PASHTU, AND TURKIC LANGUAGES.

KABUL

PEACHES

HINDU KUSH MTS

OUR HAND-WOVEN CARPETS ARE KNOWN WORLDWIDE.

WE PRODUCE FRUIT, NUTS, COTTON AND WOOL.

PAKISTAN

THE KHYBER PASS IS A FAMOUS ROUTE BETWEEN CENTRAL ASIA AND THE INDIAN SUB-CONTINENT.

K2, THE SECOND HIGHEST MOUNTAIN IN THE WORLD, IS IN PAKISTAN.

INDIA

IT WAS BUILT BY A MOGUL EMPEROR IN THE 17TH CENTURY AS A TOMB FOR HIS WIFE.

THE TAJ MAHAL TOOK 20,000 WORKERS 20 YEARS TO BUILD.

NEPAL

ISLAMABAD

THE POPULATION IS 28,000,000.

URDU, ENGLISH, PUNJABI, SINDHI, PUSHTU, AND BALOCHI ARE OUR LANGUAGES.

WE HAVE VERY HOT SUMMERS AND COLD WINTERS, AND GREAT CHANGES IN TEMPERATURE BETWEEN NIGHT AND DAY.

OUR POPULATION IS 164,000,000.

BADSHAHI MOSQUE

JAMIA MOSQUE

WHEAT

COTTON

COTTON

PEANUTS

THAR DESERT

NEW DELHI

MILLET

OUR OFFICIAL LANGUAGES ARE HINDI AND ENGLISH.

FIFTEEN MAJOR LANGUAGES AND ABOUT 1,650 DIALECTS ARE SPOKEN HERE, TOO.

HINDU DANCER

WE ELEPHANTS ARE TAUGHT BY "MAHOUTS" (TRAINERS) TO DO HEAVY LABOR.

GREEN TURTLE

THE 18-FOOT KING COBRA IS THE LONGEST POISONOUS SNAKE IN THE WORLD.

SITAR MUSICIANS

IN MAY AND JUNE, TEMPERATURES CAN REACH 120°F.

ONLY ABOUT 4,000 TIGERS ARE LEFT IN INDIA. 80 YEARS AGO THERE WERE OVER 40,000.

OUR POPULATION IS 1,110,000,000, WHICH IS SECOND ONLY TO CHINA'S.

MUMBAI IS INDIA'S MOST POPULOUS CITY, WITH MORE THAN 18 MILLION PEOPLE.

ARABIAN SEA

MUMBAI (BOMBAY)

TEA

TRADITIONAL DRESS FOR WOMEN IS THE SARI.

THERE ARE NEARLY 600,000 VILLAGES IN INDIA.

PEPPER

COWS ARE SACRED ANIMALS AND ARE NEVER KILLED.

CIVILIZATION HERE CAN BE TRACED BACK MORE THAN 5,000 YEARS.

WE HAVE A CARGO OF TEA, GEMSTONES, AND SPICES FROM SRI LANKA.

THAT'S A DHOW, AN ARAB SHIP.

TOBACCO

MALDIVES POP. 360,000 CAPITAL: MALÉ

WE SPEAK MALDIVIAN DHIVEHI AND ENGLISH.

THE INDIAN SUBCONTINENT

South-central Asia—where a large area of land juts into the Indian Ocean—is referred to as the Indian subcontinent. About 70 percent of the people in this heavily populated region depend on the land for their livelihood.

India is one of only two countries in the world with more than one billion people. (China is the other.) The other countries in this region are Afghanistan, Pakistan, Nepal, Bhutan, Bangladesh, and Sri Lanka. About 400 miles southwest of Sri Lanka is a group of small islands that make up the country of Maldives.

LEARN ABOUT THE INDIAN SUBCONTINENT AS YOU LOOK FOR THESE FUN ITEMS:

- ❏ Bear
- ❏ Camels (2)
- ❏ Carpets (3)
- ❏ Cow
- ❏ Dancer
- ❏ Elephants (2)
- ❏ Fish (2)
- ❏ Monkeys (2)
- ❏ Musicians (2)
- ❏ Peanuts
- ❏ Pepper
- ❏ Snakes (2)
- ❏ Soccer ball
- ❏ Rhinoceros
- ❏ Turtle
- ❏ Umbrella

MT. EVEREST SITS ON THE BORDER BETWEEN NEPAL AND TIBET.

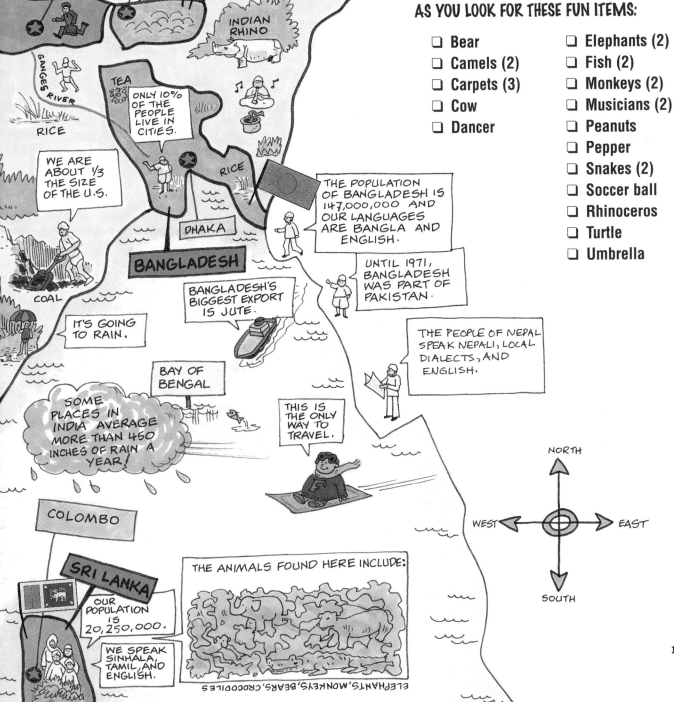

THE POPULATION OF BHUTAN IS 2,300,000.

THEY SPEAK DZONGKHA.

ONLY 3% OF THIS RUGGED, MOUNTAINOUS LAND IS ARABLE.

NEPAL HAS 8 OF THE WORLD'S 10 HIGHEST MOUNTAINS.

BHUTAN

KATHMANDU

THIMPHU

INDIAN RHINO

GANGES RIVER

RICE

TEA

ONLY 10% OF THE PEOPLE LIVE IN CITIES.

WE ARE ABOUT 1/3 THE SIZE OF THE U.S.

RICE

THE POPULATION OF BANGLADESH IS 147,000,000 AND OUR LANGUAGES ARE BANGLA AND ENGLISH.

DHAKA

BANGLADESH

UNTIL 1971, BANGLADESH WAS PART OF PAKISTAN.

COAL

BANGLADESH'S BIGGEST EXPORT IS JUTE.

IT'S GOING TO RAIN.

THE PEOPLE OF NEPAL SPEAK NEPALI, LOCAL DIALECTS, AND ENGLISH.

BAY OF BENGAL

SOME PLACES IN INDIA AVERAGE MORE THAN 450 INCHES OF RAIN A YEAR!

THIS IS THE ONLY WAY TO TRAVEL.

NORTH

WEST EAST

SOUTH

COLOMBO

SRI LANKA

OUR POPULATION IS 20,250,000.

THE ANIMALS FOUND HERE INCLUDE:

WE SPEAK SINHALA, TAMIL, AND ENGLISH.

ELEPHANTS, MONKEYS, BEARS, CROCODILES

CHINA AND NORTHEASTERN ASIA

China is the world's third-largest country in land area and first in population. (One out of every five people on Earth lives in China.) Much of China and the Korean peninsula is mountainous. The world's highest mountains, the Himalayas, are in Tibet, a region of China.

LEARN ABOUT CHINA AND NORTHEASTERN ASIA AS YOU LOOK FOR THESE FUN ITEMS:

- ❑ Bicycles (5)
- ❑ Camel
- ❑ Clay soldiers
- ❑ Ducks (3)
- ❑ Flying saucer
- ❑ Genghis Khan
- ❑ Horse
- ❑ Junk
- ❑ Mongol tent
- ❑ Pandas (2)
- ❑ Vulture
- ❑ Yaks (2)

16

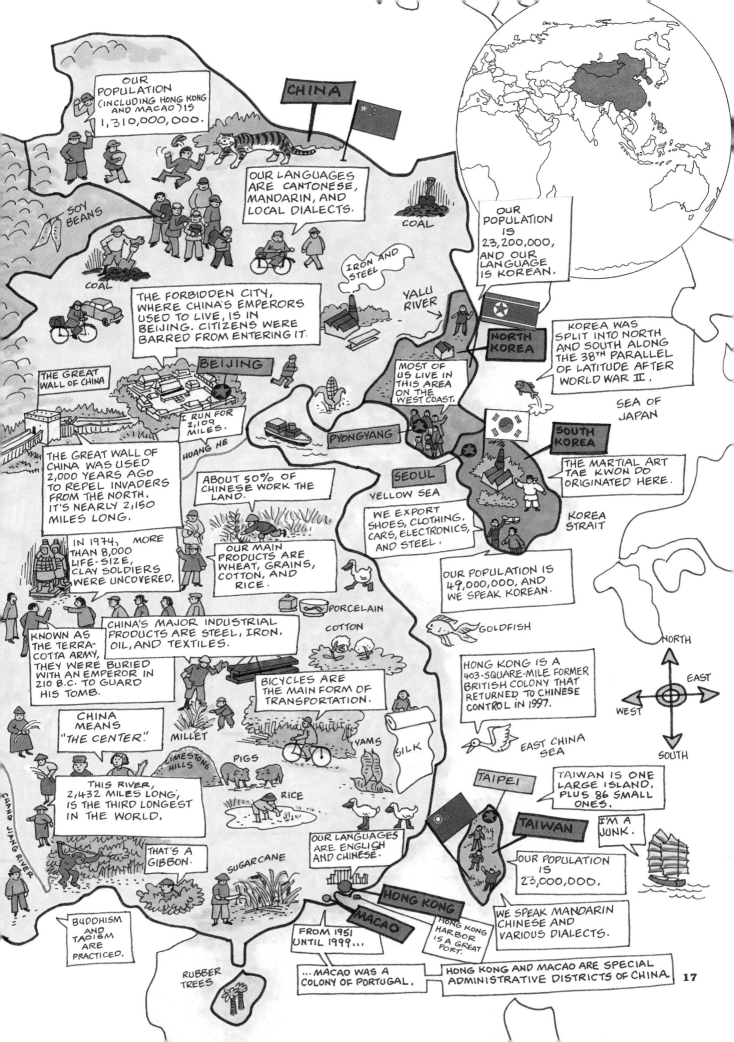

OUR POPULATION (INCLUDING HONG KONG AND MACAO) IS 1,310,000,000.

CHINA

OUR LANGUAGES ARE CANTONESE, MANDARIN, AND LOCAL DIALECTS.

SOY BEANS

COAL

COAL

IRON AND STEEL

YALU RIVER

THE FORBIDDEN CITY, WHERE CHINA'S EMPERORS USED TO LIVE, IS IN BEIJING. CITIZENS WERE BARRED FROM ENTERING IT.

THE GREAT WALL OF CHINA

BEIJING

NORTH KOREA

OUR POPULATION IS 23,200,000, AND OUR LANGUAGE IS KOREAN.

KOREA WAS SPLIT INTO NORTH AND SOUTH ALONG THE 38TH PARALLEL OF LATITUDE AFTER WORLD WAR II.

MOST OF US LIVE IN THIS AREA ON THE WEST COAST.

SEA OF JAPAN

I RUN FOR 2,109 MILES.

HUANG HE

PYONGYANG

SEOUL

SOUTH KOREA

THE GREAT WALL OF CHINA WAS USED 2,000 YEARS AGO TO REPEL INVADERS FROM THE NORTH. IT'S NEARLY 2,150 MILES LONG.

ABOUT 50% OF CHINESE WORK THE LAND.

YELLOW SEA

THE MARTIAL ART TAE KWON DO ORIGINATED HERE.

KOREA STRAIT

IN 1974, MORE THAN 8,000 LIFE-SIZE, CLAY SOLDIERS WERE UNCOVERED.

OUR MAIN PRODUCTS ARE WHEAT, GRAINS, COTTON, AND RICE.

WE EXPORT SHOES, CLOTHING, CARS, ELECTRONICS, AND STEEL.

PORCELAIN

OUR POPULATION IS 49,000,000, AND WE SPEAK KOREAN.

COTTON

KNOWN AS THE TERRA-COTTA ARMY, THEY WERE BURIED WITH AN EMPEROR IN 210 B.C. TO GUARD HIS TOMB.

CHINA'S MAJOR INDUSTRIAL PRODUCTS ARE STEEL, IRON, OIL, AND TEXTILES.

GOLDFISH

NORTH

EAST

WEST

BICYCLES ARE THE MAIN FORM OF TRANSPORTATION.

HONG KONG IS A 403-SQUARE-MILE FORMER BRITISH COLONY THAT RETURNED TO CHINESE CONTROL IN 1997.

CHINA MEANS "THE CENTER."

MILLET

LIMESTONE HILLS

YAMS

SILK

EAST CHINA SEA

SOUTH

PIGS

CHANG JIANG RIVER

THIS RIVER, 2,432 MILES LONG, IS THE THIRD LONGEST IN THE WORLD.

THAT'S A GIBBON.

RICE

TAIPEI

TAIWAN IS ONE LARGE ISLAND, PLUS 86 SMALL ONES.

TAIWAN

I'M A JUNK.

SUGARCANE

OUR LANGUAGES ARE ENGLISH AND CHINESE.

OUR POPULATION IS 23,000,000.

BUDDHISM AND TAOISM ARE PRACTICED.

HONG KONG

MACAO

HONG KONG HARBOR IS A GREAT PORT.

WE SPEAK MANDARIN CHINESE AND VARIOUS DIALECTS.

FROM 1951 UNTIL 1999...

RUBBER TREES

...MACAO WAS A COLONY OF PORTUGAL.

HONG KONG AND MACAO ARE SPECIAL ADMINISTRATIVE DISTRICTS OF CHINA.

17

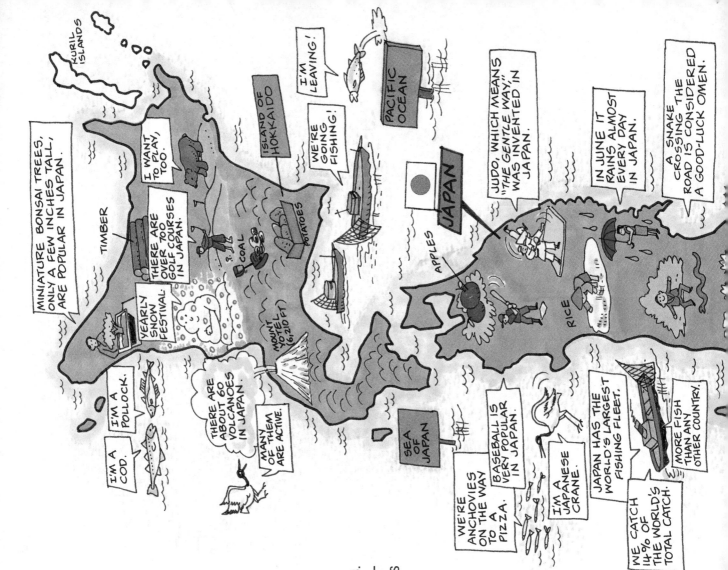

JAPAN

Japan consists of four main islands and about 4,000 smaller ones. This leading industrial country, which is almost as large as California, is densely populated. Most of the people live in the big cities on Honshu Island and in the flat coastal areas.

LEARN ABOUT JAPAN AS YOU LOOK FOR THESE FUN ITEMS:

- ☐ Anchovies
- ☐ Baseball bat
- ☐ Brown bear
- ☐ Cod
- ☐ Cook
- ☐ Crab
- ☐ Cranes (2)
- ☐ Dollar sign
- ☐ Golfer
- ☐ Octopus
- ☐ Skier
- ☐ Snake
- ☐ Snow sculpture
- ☐ Squid
- ☐ Sumo wrestler
- ☐ Tofu
- ☐ Turtle
- ☐ Umbrellas (2)

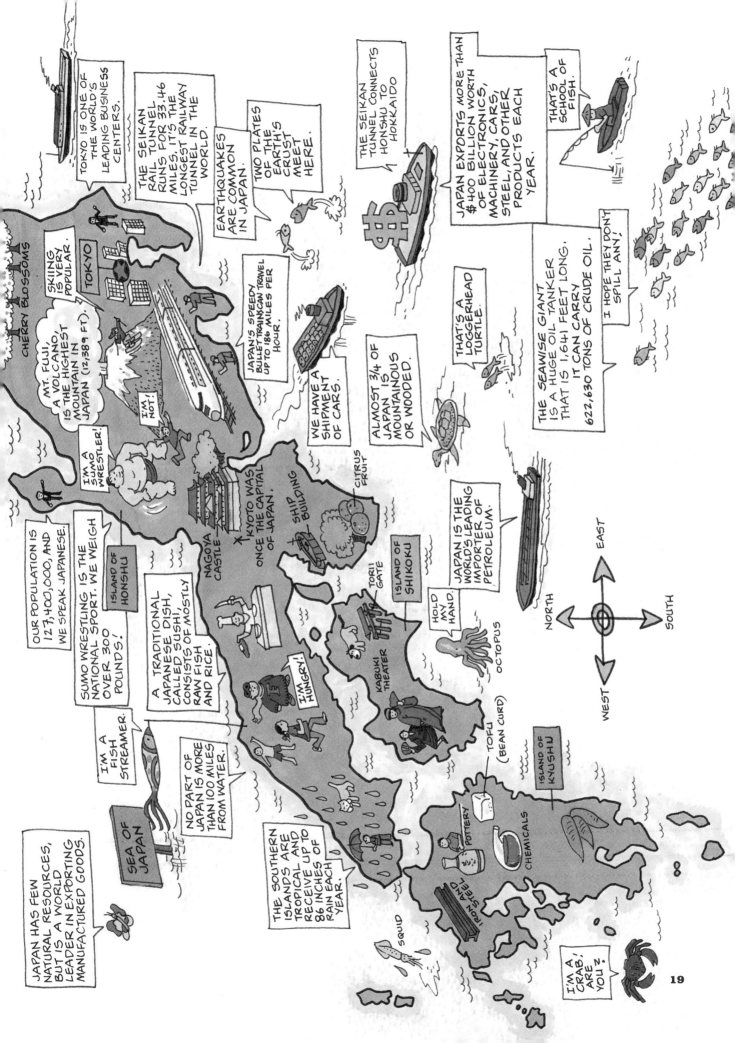

19

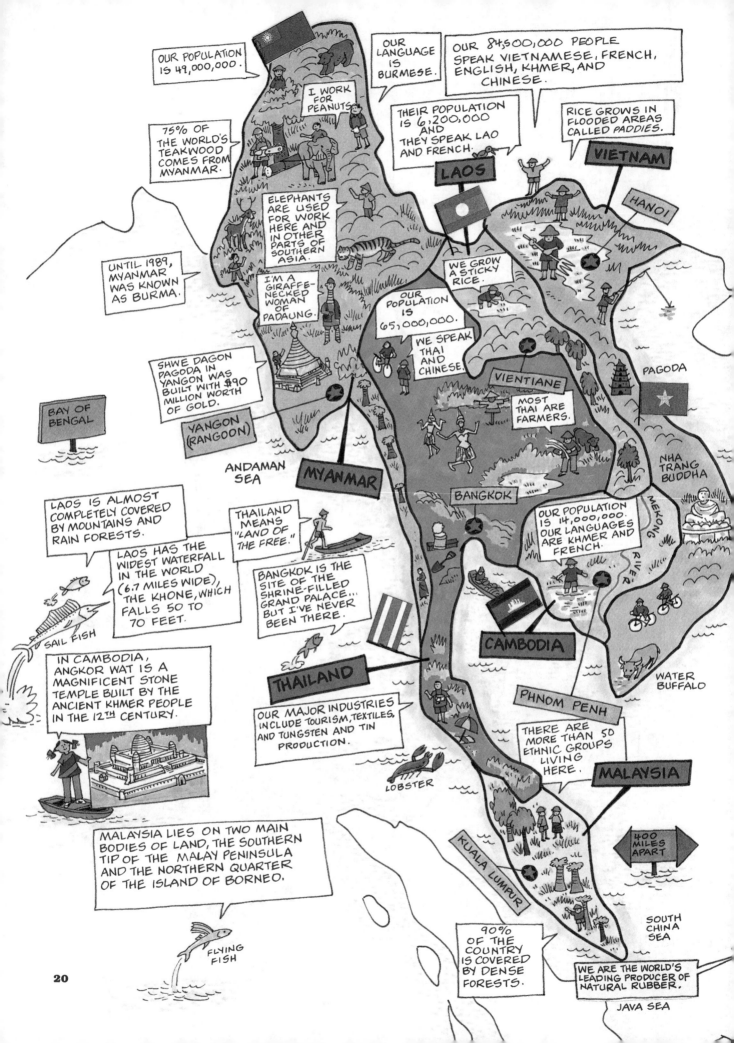

SOUTHEAST ASIA

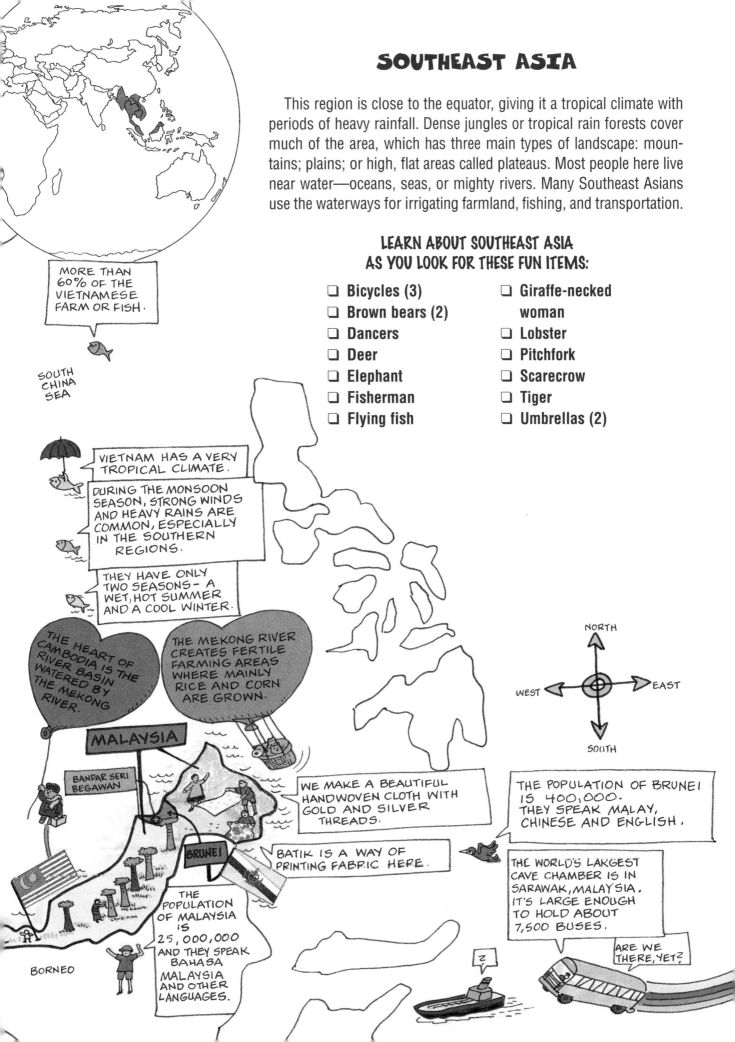

This region is close to the equator, giving it a tropical climate with periods of heavy rainfall. Dense jungles or tropical rain forests cover much of the area, which has three main types of landscape: mountains; plains; or high, flat areas called plateaus. Most people here live near water—oceans, seas, or mighty rivers. Many Southeast Asians use the waterways for irrigating farmland, fishing, and transportation.

LEARN ABOUT SOUTHEAST ASIA
AS YOU LOOK FOR THESE FUN ITEMS:

- ❏ Bicycles (3)
- ❏ Brown bears (2)
- ❏ Dancers
- ❏ Deer
- ❏ Elephant
- ❏ Fisherman
- ❏ Flying fish
- ❏ Giraffe-necked woman
- ❏ Lobster
- ❏ Pitchfork
- ❏ Scarecrow
- ❏ Tiger
- ❏ Umbrellas (2)

MORE THAN 60% OF THE VIETNAMESE FARM OR FISH.

SOUTH CHINA SEA

VIETNAM HAS A VERY TROPICAL CLIMATE.

DURING THE MONSOON SEASON, STRONG WINDS AND HEAVY RAINS ARE COMMON, ESPECIALLY IN THE SOUTHERN REGIONS.

THEY HAVE ONLY TWO SEASONS— A WET, HOT SUMMER AND A COOL WINTER.

THE HEART OF CAMBODIA IS THE RIVER BASIN WATERED BY THE MEKONG RIVER.

THE MEKONG RIVER CREATES FERTILE FARMING AREAS WHERE MAINLY RICE AND CORN ARE GROWN.

NORTH
WEST
EAST
SOUTH

MALAYSIA

BANDAR SERI BEGAWAN

WE MAKE A BEAUTIFUL HANDWOVEN CLOTH WITH GOLD AND SILVER THREADS.

THE POPULATION OF BRUNEI IS 400,000. THEY SPEAK MALAY, CHINESE AND ENGLISH.

BRUNEI

BATIK IS A WAY OF PRINTING FABRIC HERE.

THE WORLD'S LARGEST CAVE CHAMBER IS IN SARAWAK, MALAYSIA. IT'S LARGE ENOUGH TO HOLD ABOUT 7,500 BUSES.

THE POPULATION OF MALAYSIA IS 25,000,000 AND THEY SPEAK BAHASA MALAYSIA AND OTHER LANGUAGES.

BORNEO

ARE WE THERE, YET?

Z

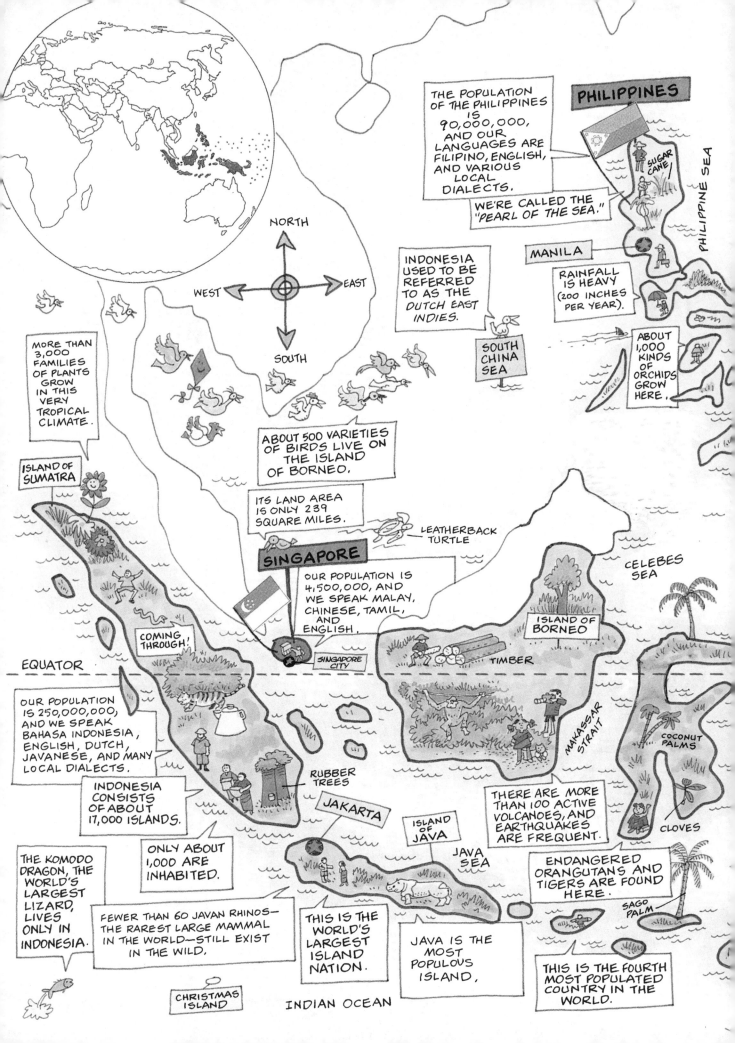

THE POPULATION OF THE PHILIPPINES IS 90,000,000, AND OUR LANGUAGES ARE FILIPINO, ENGLISH, AND VARIOUS LOCAL DIALECTS.

PHILIPPINES

WE'RE CALLED THE "PEARL OF THE SEA."

SUGAR CANE

PHILIPPINE SEA

INDONESIA USED TO BE REFERRED TO AS THE DUTCH EAST INDIES.

MANILA

RAINFALL IS HEAVY (200 INCHES PER YEAR).

SOUTH CHINA SEA

ABOUT 1,000 KINDS OF ORCHIDS GROW HERE.

NORTH

WEST

EAST

SOUTH

MORE THAN 3,000 FAMILIES OF PLANTS GROW IN THIS VERY TROPICAL CLIMATE.

ABOUT 500 VARIETIES OF BIRDS LIVE ON THE ISLAND OF BORNEO.

ISLAND OF SUMATRA

ITS LAND AREA IS ONLY 239 SQUARE MILES.

LEATHERBACK TURTLE

SINGAPORE

OUR POPULATION IS 4,500,000, AND WE SPEAK MALAY, CHINESE, TAMIL, AND ENGLISH.

CELEBES SEA

ISLAND OF BORNEO

COMING THROUGH!

EQUATOR

SINGAPORE CITY

TIMBER

MAKASSAR STRAIT

COCONUT PALMS

OUR POPULATION IS 250,000,000, AND WE SPEAK BAHASA INDONESIA, ENGLISH, DUTCH, JAVANESE, AND MANY LOCAL DIALECTS.

RUBBER TREES

INDONESIA CONSISTS OF ABOUT 17,000 ISLANDS.

JAKARTA

ISLAND OF JAVA

THERE ARE MORE THAN 100 ACTIVE VOLCANOES, AND EARTHQUAKES ARE FREQUENT.

CLOVES

THE KOMODO DRAGON, THE WORLD'S LARGEST LIZARD, LIVES ONLY IN INDONESIA.

ONLY ABOUT 1,000 ARE INHABITED.

JAVA SEA

ENDANGERED ORANGUTANS AND TIGERS ARE FOUND HERE.

FEWER THAN 60 JAVAN RHINOS— THE RAREST LARGE MAMMAL IN THE WORLD—STILL EXIST IN THE WILD.

THIS IS THE WORLD'S LARGEST ISLAND NATION.

JAVA IS THE MOST POPULOUS ISLAND.

SAGO PALM

CHRISTMAS ISLAND

INDIAN OCEAN

THIS IS THE FOURTH MOST POPULATED COUNTRY IN THE WORLD.

INDONESIA AND PACIFIC ISLAND NATIONS

Indonesia, Singapore, the Philippines, and East Timor are part of Asia. Papua New Guinea and many small island nations scattered in this area of the Pacific Ocean are part of a region called Oceania. *(See p. 5 for a list of all the countries of Oceania.)* Most of this area has a hot, wet, tropical climate.

LEARN ABOUT INDONESIA AND PACIFIC ISLAND NATIONS AS YOU LOOK FOR THESE FUN ITEMS:

- ❑ Airplane
- ❑ Coffeepot
- ❑ Fish (2)
- ❑ Kite
- ❑ Orangutan
- ❑ Photographer
- ❑ Rhinoceros
- ❑ Shark fins (4)
- ❑ Tiger
- ❑ Tree kangaroo
- ❑ Turtle
- ❑ Volcanoes (2)

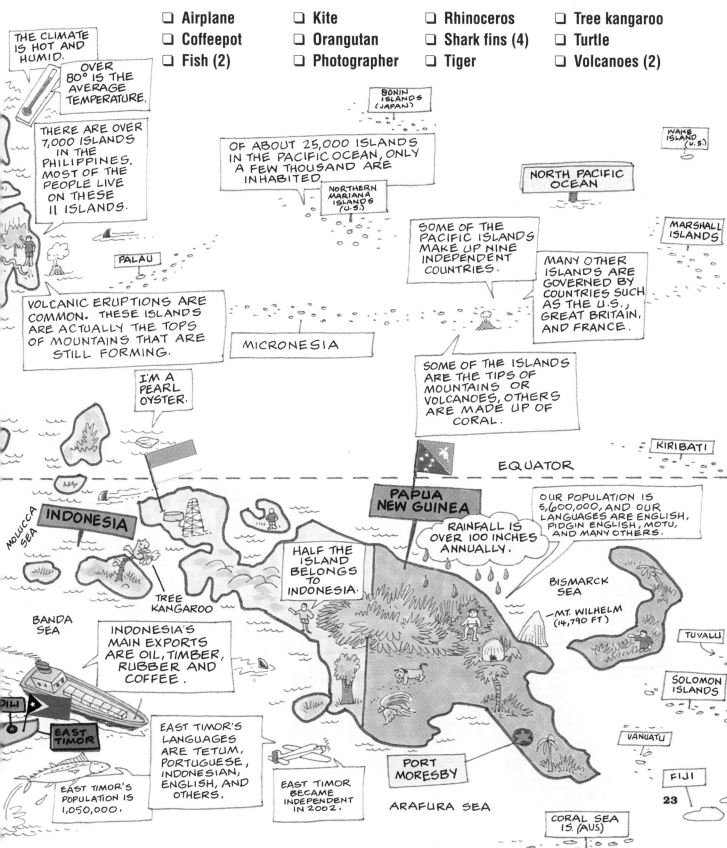

THE CLIMATE IS HOT AND HUMID.

OVER 80° IS THE AVERAGE TEMPERATURE.

THERE ARE OVER 7,000 ISLANDS IN THE PHILIPPINES, MOST OF THE PEOPLE LIVE ON THESE 11 ISLANDS.

BONIN ISLANDS (JAPAN)

OF ABOUT 25,000 ISLANDS IN THE PACIFIC OCEAN, ONLY A FEW THOUSAND ARE INHABITED.

NORTHERN MARIANA ISLANDS (U.S.)

WAKE ISLAND (U.S.)

NORTH PACIFIC OCEAN

MARSHALL ISLANDS

SOME OF THE PACIFIC ISLANDS MAKE UP NINE INDEPENDENT COUNTRIES.

MANY OTHER ISLANDS ARE GOVERNED BY COUNTRIES SUCH AS THE U.S., GREAT BRITAIN, AND FRANCE.

PALAU

VOLCANIC ERUPTIONS ARE COMMON. THESE ISLANDS ARE ACTUALLY THE TOPS OF MOUNTAINS THAT ARE STILL FORMING.

MICRONESIA

SOME OF THE ISLANDS ARE THE TIPS OF MOUNTAINS OR VOLCANOES, OTHERS ARE MADE UP OF CORAL.

I'M A PEARL OYSTER.

KIRIBATI

EQUATOR

PAPUA NEW GUINEA

OUR POPULATION IS 5,600,000, AND OUR LANGUAGES ARE ENGLISH, PIDGIN ENGLISH, MOTU, AND MANY OTHERS.

MOLUCCA SEA

INDONESIA

HALF THE ISLAND BELONGS TO INDONESIA.

RAINFALL IS OVER 100 INCHES ANNUALLY.

BISMARCK SEA

MT. WILHELM (14,790 FT)

TREE KANGAROO

BANDA SEA

INDONESIA'S MAIN EXPORTS ARE OIL, TIMBER, RUBBER AND COFFEE.

TUVALU

SOLOMON ISLANDS

DILI

EAST TIMOR

EAST TIMOR'S LANGUAGES ARE TETUM, PORTUGUESE, INDONESIAN, ENGLISH, AND OTHERS.

EAST TIMOR'S POPULATION IS 1,050,000.

EAST TIMOR BECAME INDEPENDENT IN 2002.

PORT MORESBY

ARAFURA SEA

VANUATU

FIJI

CORAL SEA IS. (AUS)

23

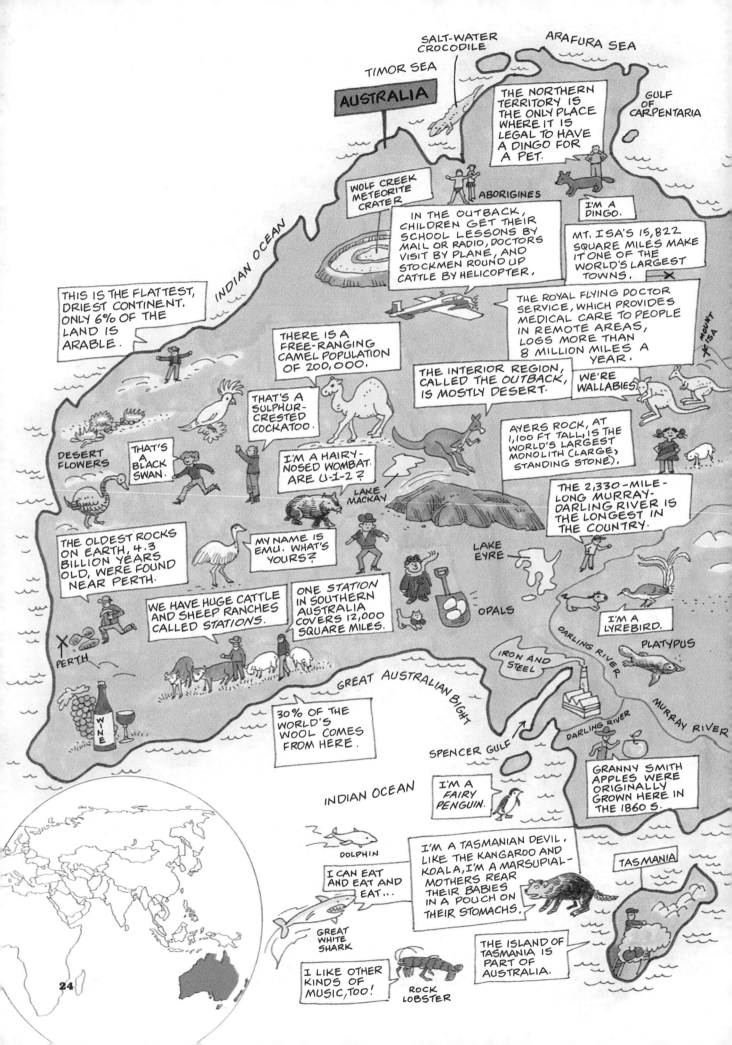

AUSTRALIA AND NEW ZEALAND

Australia is the only country that is also a continent. Its nickname, "Down Under," comes from the fact that the entire continent lies south of the equator.

Millions of years ago, Australia broke off from the other continents. Its first settlers, called Aborigines *(AB-uh-RIJ-uh-neez)*, arrived about 40,000 years ago, from islands in the Pacific Ocean. (*Ab origine* means "from the beginning.") Their descendants still live in Australia today.

New Zealand lies about 1,000 miles southeast of Australia. Both countries are in a region called Oceania.

LEARN ABOUT AUSTRALIA AND NEW ZEALAND AS YOU LOOK FOR THESE FUN ITEMS:

- ❏ **Banana**
- ❏ **Camel**
- ❏ **Cockatoo**
- ❏ **Emu**
- ❏ **Kangaroo**
- ❏ **Koalas (2)**
- ❏ **Lyrebird**
- ❏ **Penguin**
- ❏ **Platypus**
- ❏ **Sharks (2)**
- ❏ **Skier**
- ❏ **Swan**
- ❏ **Tasmanian devil**
- ❏ **Volcano**
- ❏ **Wallabies (2)**
- ❏ **Windsurfer**
- ❏ **Wombat**

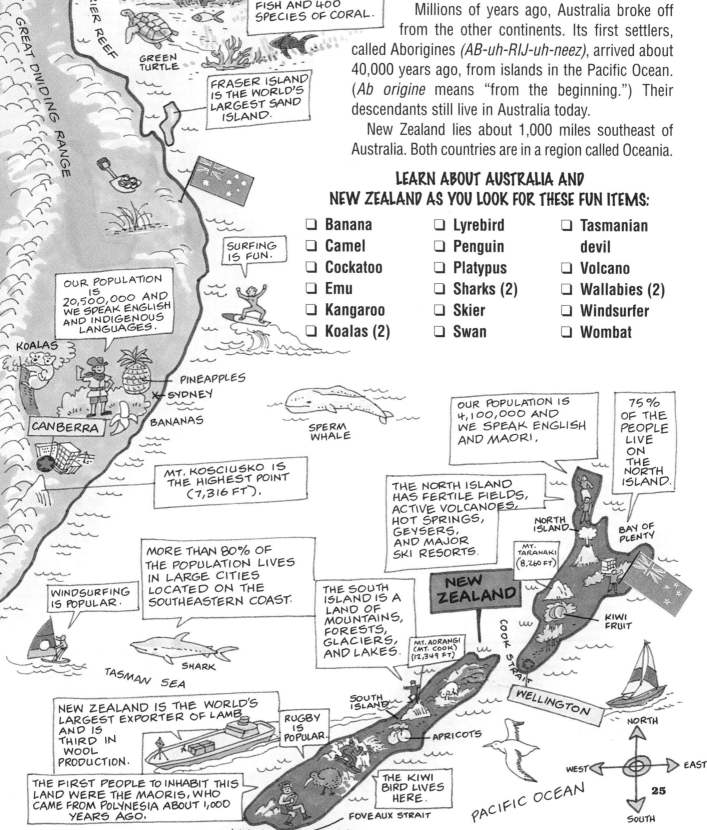

ABORIGINAL CAVE PAINTINGS

THE GREAT BARRIER REEF IS HERE. IT STRETCHES FOR 1,250 MILES.

GREAT BARRIER REEF

GREAT DIVIDING RANGE

THIS REEF IS THE BIGGEST STRUCTURE BUILT BY LIVING CREATURES IN THE WORLD. IT IS HOME TO 1500 SPECIES OF FISH AND 400 SPECIES OF CORAL.

GREEN TURTLE

FRASER ISLAND IS THE WORLD'S LARGEST SAND ISLAND.

SURFING IS FUN.

OUR POPULATION IS 20,500,000 AND WE SPEAK ENGLISH AND INDIGENOUS LANGUAGES.

KOALAS

PINEAPPLES

SYDNEY

CANBERRA

BANANAS

SPERM WHALE

MT. KOSCIUSKO IS THE HIGHEST POINT (7,316 FT).

MORE THAN 80% OF THE POPULATION LIVES IN LARGE CITIES LOCATED ON THE SOUTHEASTERN COAST.

WINDSURFING IS POPULAR.

THE SOUTH ISLAND IS A LAND OF MOUNTAINS, FORESTS, GLACIERS, AND LAKES.

SHARK

TASMAN SEA

NEW ZEALAND IS THE WORLD'S LARGEST EXPORTER OF LAMB AND IS THIRD IN WOOL PRODUCTION.

RUGBY IS POPULAR.

THE FIRST PEOPLE TO INHABIT THIS LAND WERE THE MAORIS, WHO CAME FROM POLYNESIA ABOUT 1,000 YEARS AGO.

SOUTH ISLAND

MT. AORANGI (MT. COOK) (12,349 FT)

APRICOTS

FOVEAUX STRAIT

OUR POPULATION IS 4,100,000 AND WE SPEAK ENGLISH AND MAORI.

75% OF THE PEOPLE LIVE ON THE NORTH ISLAND.

THE NORTH ISLAND HAS FERTILE FIELDS, ACTIVE VOLCANOES, HOT SPRINGS, GEYSERS, AND MAJOR SKI RESORTS.

NORTH ISLAND

BAY OF PLENTY

MT. TARANAKI (8,260 FT)

NEW ZEALAND

KIWI FRUIT

COOK STRAIT

WELLINGTON

THE KIWI BIRD LIVES HERE.

NORTH

WEST

EAST

SOUTH

PACIFIC OCEAN

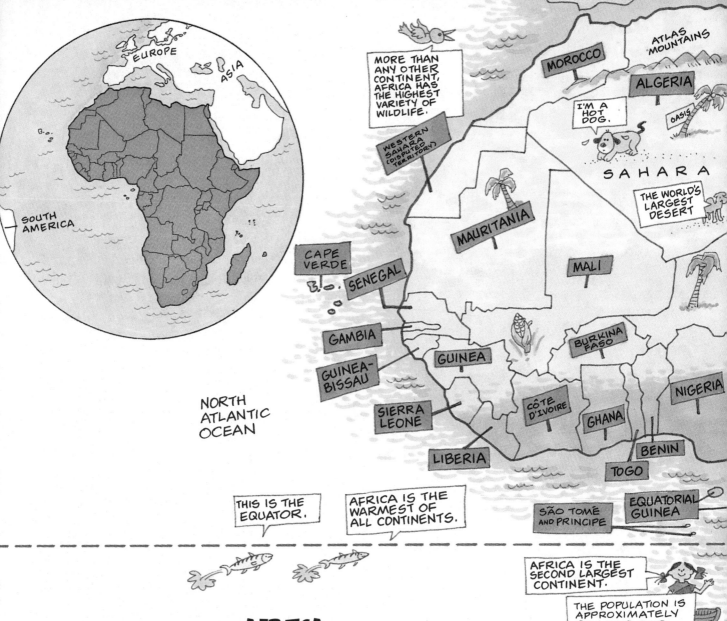

AFRICA

Once an unexplored and mysterious place to Europeans, Africa was known as the "Dark Continent." By the 19th century, European powers influenced or controlled much of Africa. However, starting in the late 1950s, country after country in Africa achieved its independence. The continent now is home to 53 independent nations. Africa's newest country, Eritrea, became independent in 1993, when it split from Ethiopia.

LEARN ABOUT AFRICA AS YOU LOOK FOR THESE FUN ITEMS:

- ❑ Atlas Mountains
- ❑ Banana
- ❑ Butterfly
- ❑ Elephant
- ❑ Gold bar
- ❑ Indian Ocean

- ❑ Mount Kilimanjaro
- ❑ Nile River
- ❑ Oil wells (2)
- ❑ Palm trees (4)
- ❑ Pyramid
- ❑ Rain cloud

- ❑ Rhinoceros
- ❑ Sea horse
- ❑ Sheep (2)
- ❑ Suez Canal
- ❑ Umbrella
- ❑ Zebra

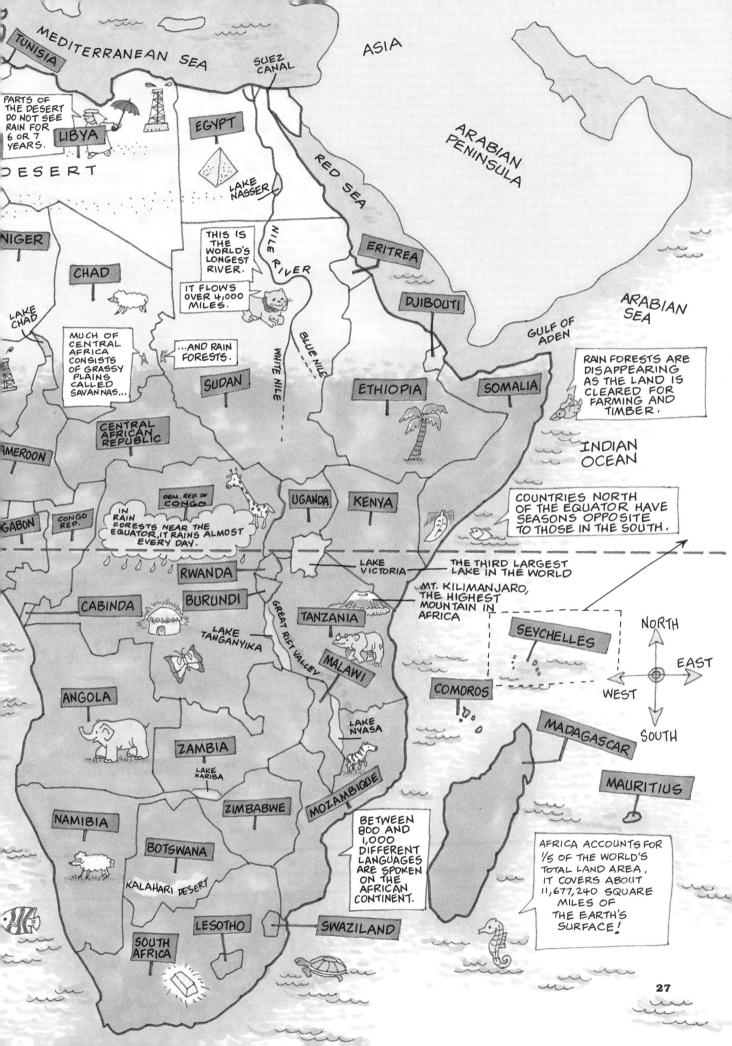

MEDITERRANEAN SEA

ASIA

TUNISIA

SUEZ CANAL

LIBYA

PARTS OF THE DESERT DO NOT SEE RAIN FOR 6 OR 7 YEARS.

DESERT

EGYPT

LAKE NASSER

ARABIAN PENINSULA

RED SEA

NIGER

CHAD

THIS IS THE WORLD'S LONGEST RIVER.

IT FLOWS OVER 4,000 MILES.

NILE RIVER

ERITREA

ARABIAN SEA

LAKE CHAD

MUCH OF CENTRAL AFRICA CONSISTS OF GRASSY PLAINS CALLED SAVANNAS...

...AND RAIN FORESTS.

SUDAN

WHITE NILE

BLUE NILE

DJIBOUTI

GULF OF ADEN

RAIN FORESTS ARE DISAPPEARING AS THE LAND IS CLEARED FOR FARMING AND TIMBER.

CAMEROON

CENTRAL AFRICAN REPUBLIC

ETHIOPIA

SOMALIA

INDIAN OCEAN

GABON

CONGO REP.

DEM. REP. OF CONGO

IN RAIN FORESTS NEAR THE EQUATOR, IT RAINS ALMOST EVERY DAY.

UGANDA

KENYA

COUNTRIES NORTH OF THE EQUATOR HAVE SEASONS OPPOSITE TO THOSE IN THE SOUTH.

RWANDA

LAKE VICTORIA

THE THIRD LARGEST LAKE IN THE WORLD

CABINDA

BURUNDI

LAKE TANGANYIKA

GREAT RIFT VALLEY

TANZANIA

MT. KILIMANJARO, THE HIGHEST MOUNTAIN IN AFRICA

SEYCHELLES

NORTH

MALAWI

WEST

EAST

ANGOLA

LAKE NYASA

COMOROS

SOUTH

MADAGASCAR

ZAMBIA

LAKE KARIBA

ZIMBABWE

MOZAMBIQUE

MAURITIUS

NAMIBIA

BETWEEN 800 AND 1,000 DIFFERENT LANGUAGES ARE SPOKEN ON THE AFRICAN CONTINENT.

BOTSWANA

AFRICA ACCOUNTS FOR 1/5 OF THE WORLD'S TOTAL LAND AREA, IT COVERS ABOUT 11,677,240 SQUARE MILES OF THE EARTH'S SURFACE!

KALAHARI DESERT

LESOTHO

SWAZILAND

SOUTH AFRICA

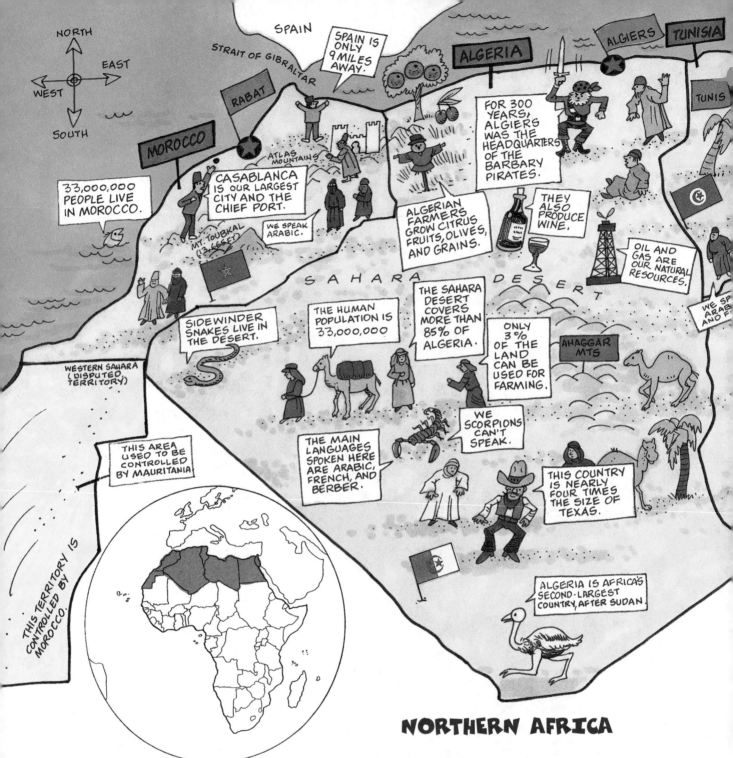

NORTHERN AFRICA

The peoples of ancient Greece, Rome, and Arabia influenced cultures in this part of Africa, and African culture—especially that of ancient Egypt—influenced them. In northern Africa today, Arabic is the dominant language and Islam is the major religion. Although Egypt is on the African continent, politically it often is considered part of the region known as the Middle East.

LEARN ABOUT NORTHERN AFRICA AS YOU LOOK FOR THESE FUN ITEMS:

- ❏ Barbary ape
- ❏ Beret
- ❏ Boats (3)
- ❏ Bunch of grapes
- ❏ Hyena
- ❏ Miner
- ❏ Mummy
- ❏ Oil wells (4)
- ❏ Orange tree
- ❏ Ostrich
- ❏ Palm trees (3)
- ❏ Pencil
- ❏ Pirate
- ❏ Pyramids (4)
- ❏ Scarecrow
- ❏ Scorpion
- ❏ Shovel
- ❏ Snake
- ❏ Thermometer

29

THE SAHEL

Just south of the Sahara Desert is a region called the Sahel, long inhabited by animal grazers and farmers. Much of the area is changing into desert as the Sahara expands southward at a rate of about three miles a year.

LEARN ABOUT THE SAHEL AS YOU LOOK FOR THESE FUN ITEMS:

- ❑ Anchor
- ❑ Basket
- ❑ Bird
- ❑ Camels (5)
- ❑ Cotton balls (3)
- ❑ Elephant
- ❑ Fisherman
- ❑ Goat
- ❑ Hippopotamus
- ❑ Lake Chad
- ❑ Niger River
- ❑ Peanuts (3)
- ❑ Periscope
- ❑ Soccer ball
- ❑ Sun
- ❑ Tent

31

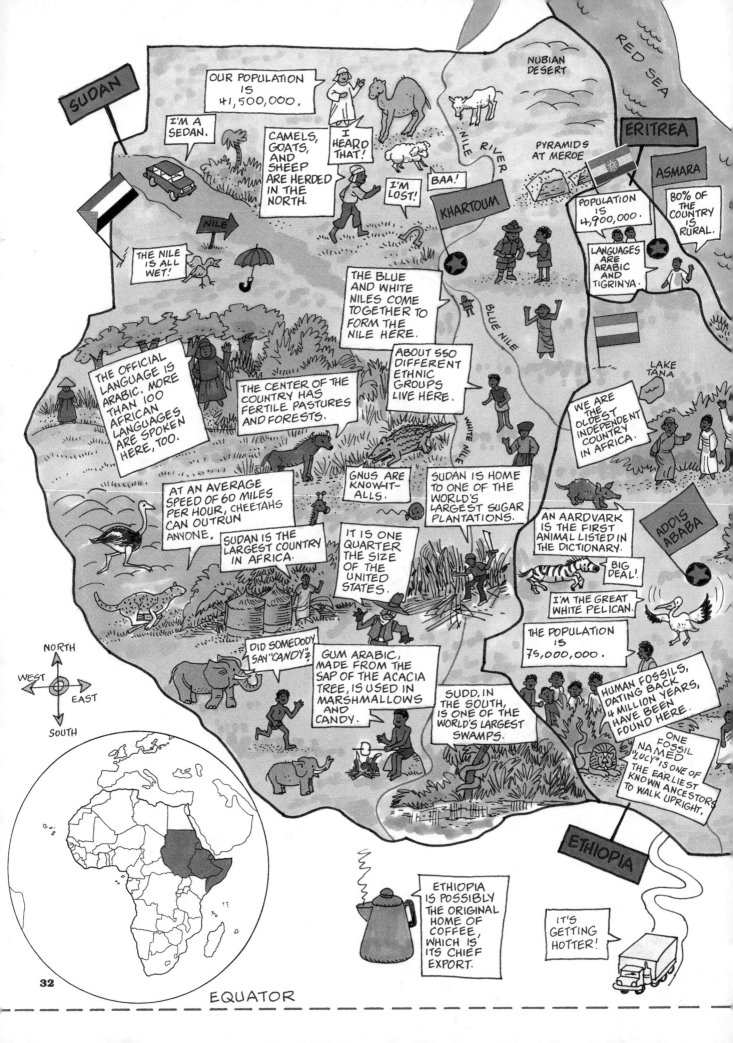

THE HORN OF AFRICA

The region along Africa's northeastern coast is known as the Horn of Africa. On maps, its shape looks like the horn of a rhinoceros jutting into the Indian Ocean.

LEARN ABOUT THE HORN OF AFRICA AS YOU LOOK FOR THESE FUN ITEMS:

- ❑ Aardvark
- ❑ Acacia tree
- ❑ Banana
- ❑ Coffeepot
- ❑ Cotton
- ❑ Giraffes (2)
- ❑ Horseshoe

- ❑ Lion
- ❑ Marshmallow
- ❑ Nile crocodile
- ❑ Nubian Desert
- ❑ Oryx
- ❑ Ostrich
- ❑ Red Sea
- ❑ Umbrella
- ❑ White Nile
- ❑ Zebra

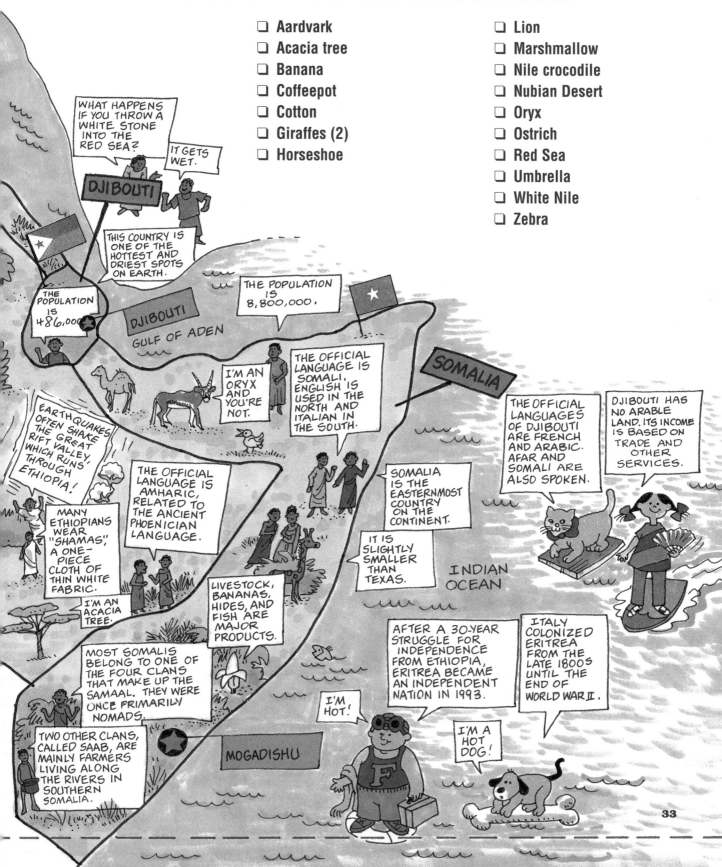

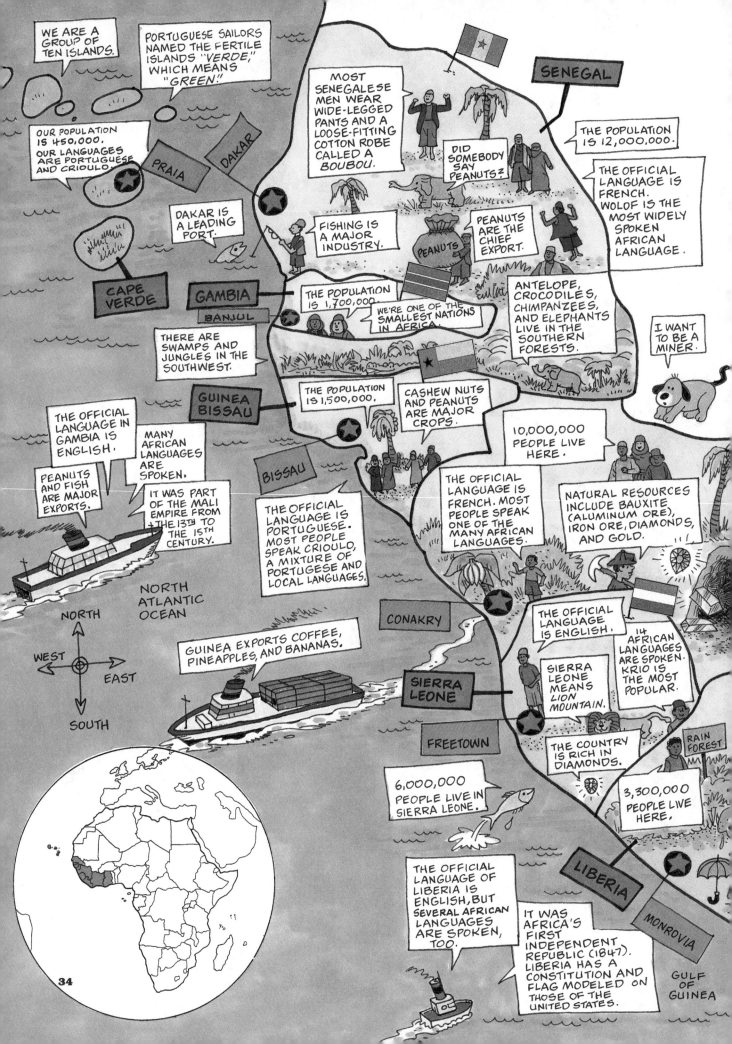

THE UPPER WEST COAST

Africa's upper west coast—the part that, seen on a map, bulges out into the Atlantic Ocean—has a landscape that varies from humid coastal plains and swamps to forested hills and plateaus. The soil is fertile, and farmers in this area grow such crops as cocoa, coffee, and peanuts.

During the era of the slave trade to the Americas, and for centuries before with other nations, coastal kingdoms of West Africa grew rich by trading slaves, gold, and ivory with Europeans.

LEARN ABOUT AFRICA'S UPPER WEST COAST AS YOU LOOK FOR THESE FUN ITEMS:

- ❑ Boats (4)
- ❑ Chocolate bar
- ❑ Coffeepot
- ❑ Crocodile
- ❑ Diamonds (4)
- ❑ Elephants (4)
- ❑ Fisherman
- ❑ Game warden
- ❑ Gold bars (3)
- ❑ Lake Volta
- ❑ Lion
- ❑ Miner
- ❑ Pygmy hippopotamus
- ❑ Rain clouds (2)
- ❑ Umbrella

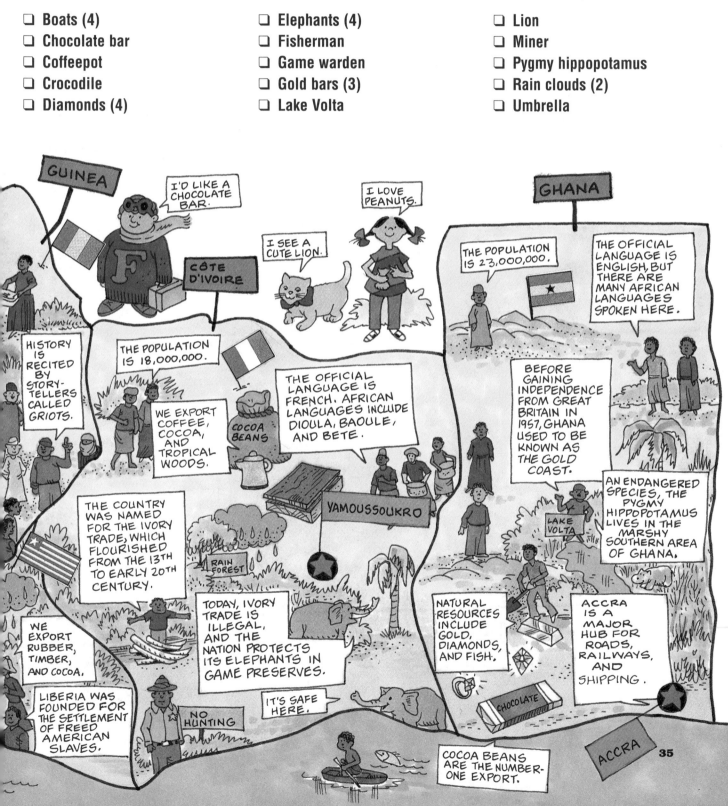

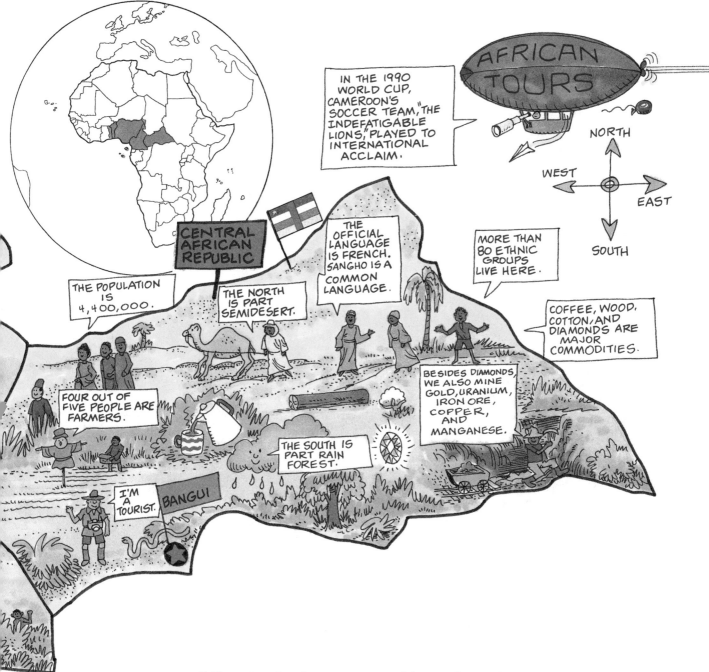

THE GULF OF GUINEA REGION

The Gulf of Guinea is a large section of the Atlantic that lies in the curve of Africa's bulging upper west coast. Many of the countries in this region share the "slave coast" history of the upper west coast countries (pp. 34-35). The gulf region has a richly varied landscape that includes old volcanic mountains, semidesert areas, swamps, tropical rain forests, and savannas. (*Savanna* is tropical or subtropical grassland.)

LEARN ABOUT AFRICA'S GULF OF GUINEA REGION AS YOU LOOK FOR THESE FUN ITEMS:

- ❏ Camera
- ❏ Cup
- ❏ Fishing poles (2)
- ❏ Giraffe
- ❏ Huts (2)
- ❏ Life preserver
- ❏ Oil wells (3)
- ❏ Paper airplane
- ❏ Red car
- ❏ Scarecrow
- ❏ Shark
- ❏ Snakes (2)
- ❏ Telescope
- ❏ Umbrellas (2)
- ❏ Volcano

EQUATORIAL AFRICA

These countries all lie on or very near the equator. A ridge of high land runs down along Lake Albert and Lake Tanganyika, splitting the region. West of the ridge are Equatorial Guinea, Gabon, Congo Republic, and the Democratic Republic of Congo. Much of the land in these countries is tropical rain forest. On and east of the ridge are Uganda, Rwanda, Burundi, Kenya, and Tanzania. The land there ranges from rain forest in the highlands to broad savanna (grasslands), where occasional dry spells can make water scarce for wildlife and humans alike.

LEARN ABOUT EQUATORIAL AFRICA AS YOU LOOK FOR THESE FUN ITEMS:

❏ Coffeepot
❏ Congo River
❏ Crocodile
❏ Elephants (4)
❏ Gorilla
❏ Lake Tanganyika
❏ Lion
❏ Mount Kilimanjaro
❏ Parrot
❏ Peacock
❏ Snake
❏ Umbrellas (3)
❏ Zanzibar
❏ Zebra

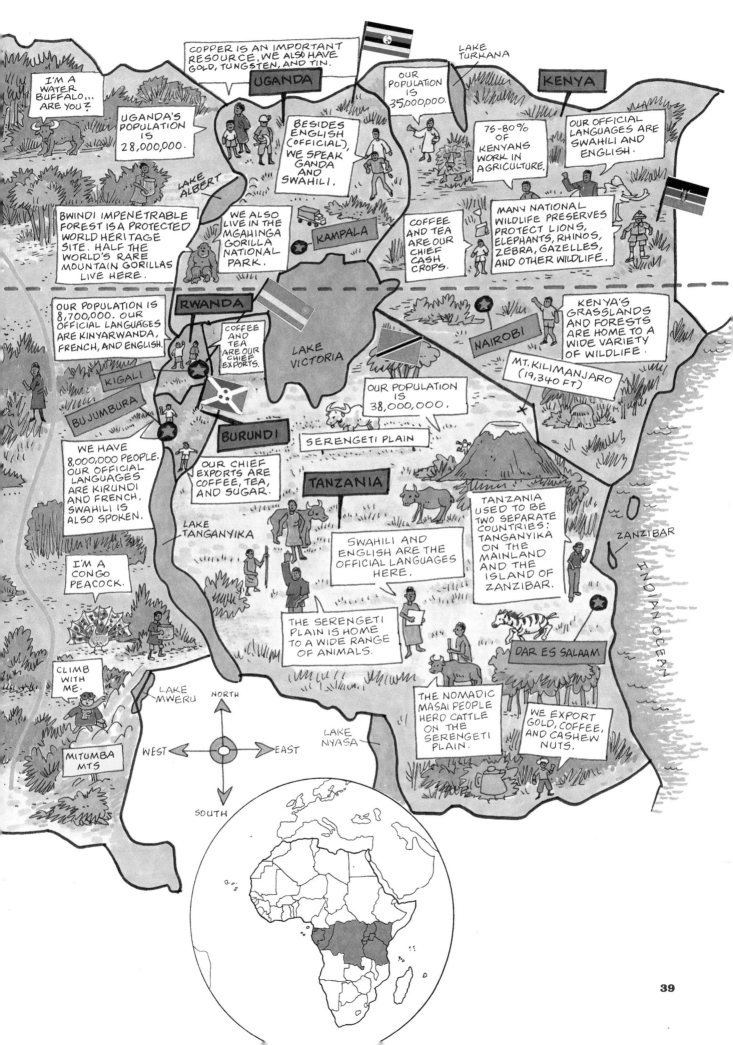

ANGOLA, ZAMBIA, MALAWI, AND MOZAMBIQUE

The region that lies south of the equatorial rain forests, between the South Atlantic Ocean and the Indian Ocean, has lots of open savanna and many farms. The area is home to antelope, elephants, giraffes, zebras, and many other animals.

LEARN ABOUT ANGOLA, ZAMBIA, MALAWI, AND MOZAMBIQUE AS YOU LOOK FOR THESE FUN ITEMS:

- ❑ Bananas (2)
- ❑ Cars (2)
- ❑ Coffee cups (2)
- ❑ Cow
- ❑ Eyeglasses
- ❑ Fish (3)

- ❑ Giraffe
- ❑ Hornbill
- ❑ Kariba Dam
- ❑ Leopard
- ❑ Rhinoceros
- ❑ Rice farmer

- ❑ Ring
- ❑ Scarecrow
- ❑ Shovel
- ❑ Snakes (2)
- ❑ Sun
- ❑ Victoria Falls

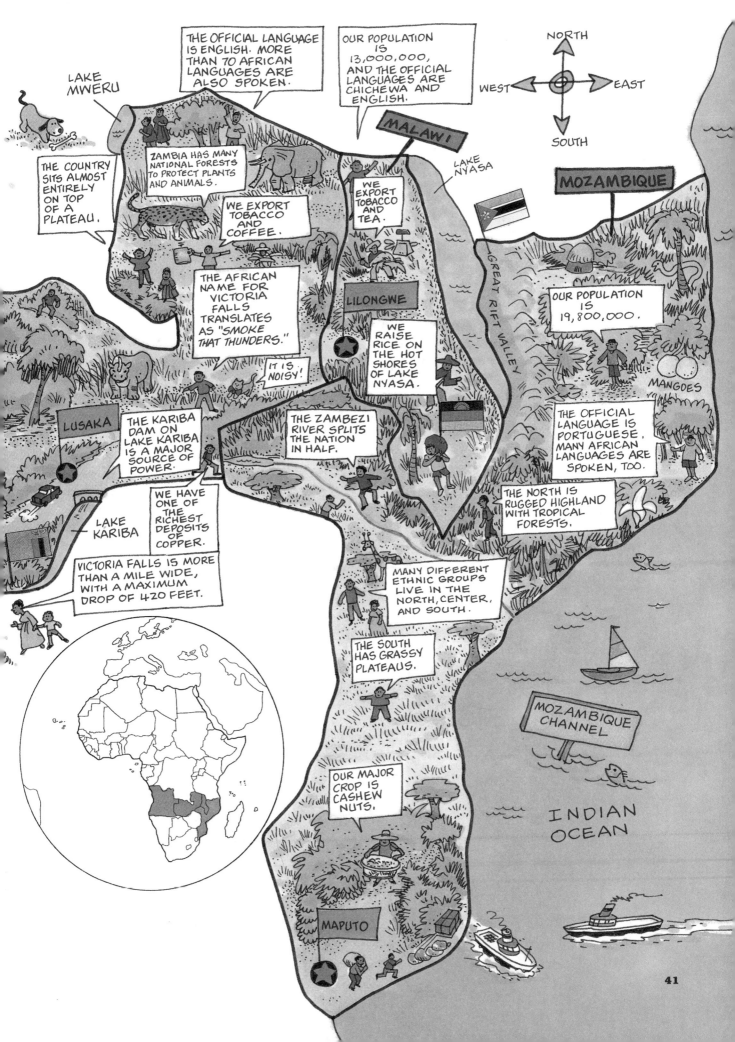

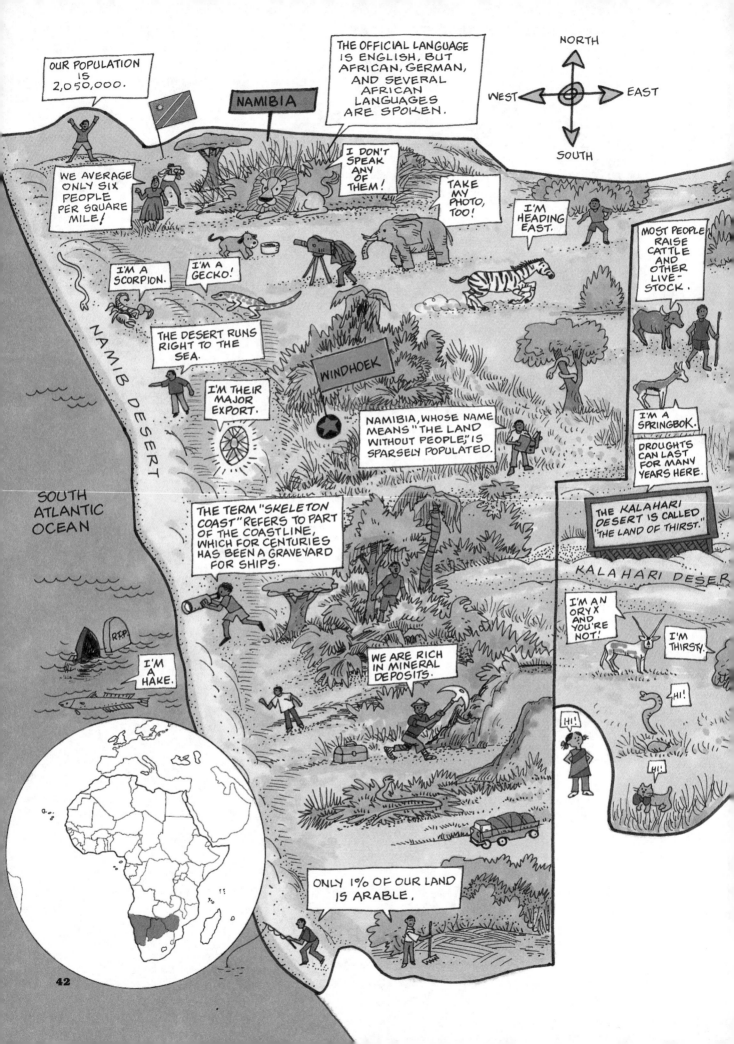

NAMIBIA, BOTSWANA, AND ZIMBABWE

Rich deposits of diamonds, gold, and minerals make this area one of the fastest-growing economic regions in Africa. Though rich in natural resources, such as diamonds and minerals, very little of the land in Namibia and Botswana is habitable. Namibia has only six people per square mile and Botswana has only seven. With its more-arable land and better-developed industries, Zimbabwe has 82 people per square mile.

LEARN ABOUT NAMIBIA, BOTSWANA, AND ZIMBABWE AS YOU LOOK FOR THESE FUN ITEMS:

- ❏ Baby
- ❏ Billboard
- ❏ Book
- ❏ Elephants (6)
- ❏ Fishing pole
- ❏ Lions (2)
- ❏ Lost snowman
- ❏ Namib Desert
- ❏ Oryx
- ❏ Picks (2)
- ❏ Rake
- ❏ Scorpion
- ❏ Shipwreck
- ❏ Snakes (5)
- ❏ Sneaker
- ❏ Truck
- ❏ Zebras (2)

SOUTH AFRICA, LESOTHO, AND SWAZILAND

The world's greatest diamond and gold mines are in South Africa, making it the richest country in Africa. The mines employ tens of thousands of men from neighboring countries.

Lesotho and Swaziland are two small, landlocked countries. One is completely surrounded by South Africa; the other is mostly so. Both are completely dependent on South Africa and Mozambique for trade routes to the ocean and other countries.

LEARN ABOUT SOUTH AFRICA, LESOTHO, AND SWAZILAND AS YOU LOOK FOR THESE FUN ITEMS:

- ❑ Cars (4)
- ❑ Citrus fruit
- ❑ Crown
- ❑ Drummer
- ❑ Giraffes (3)
- ❑ Grapes
- ❑ Guitar
- ❑ Lion
- ❑ Orange River
- ❑ Ostrich
- ❑ Pineapple
- ❑ Sailor
- ❑ Scarecrow
- ❑ Sheep (2)
- ❑ Shovel
- ❑ Table Mountain
- ❑ Tent
- ❑ Tractor
- ❑ Zebra
- ❑ Zulu warrior

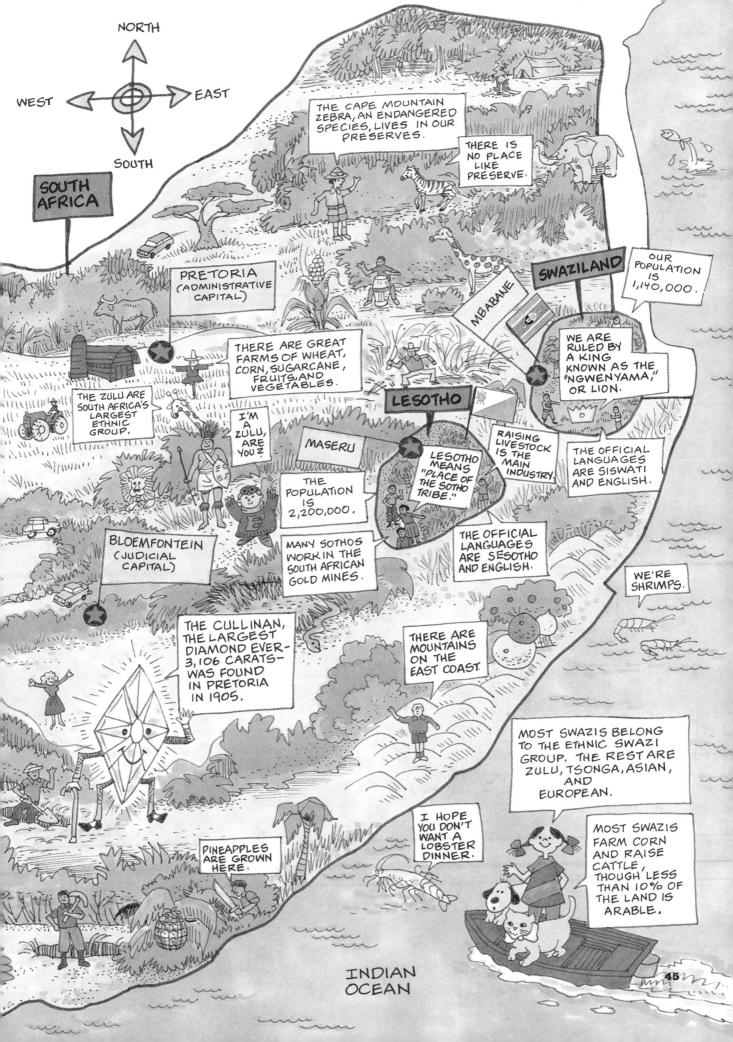

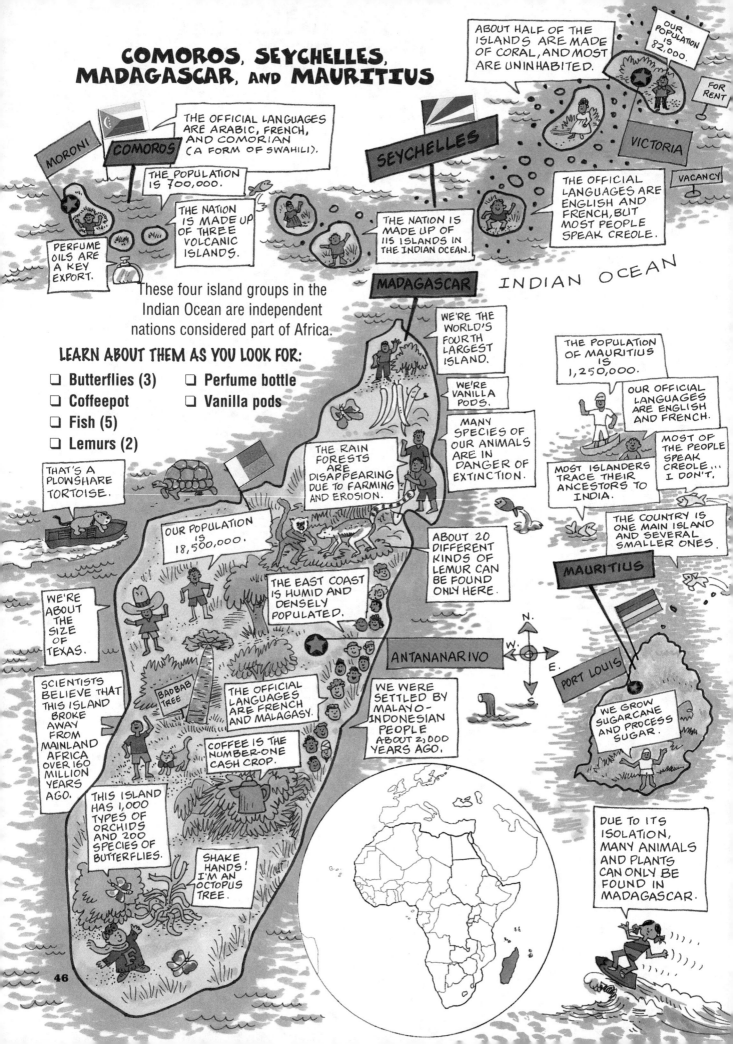

ANTARCTICA

With temperatures as low as -125° F, this continent is the coldest place on Earth. By international agreement, no one owns the land, and scientific research bases are the only inhabited places.

LEARN ABOUT ANTARCTICA AS YOU LOOK FOR THESE FUN ITEMS:

- ☐ Dinosaur
- ☐ Elephant seals (3)
- ☐ Lost mitten
- ☐ Snowman
- ☐ Snow-mobile

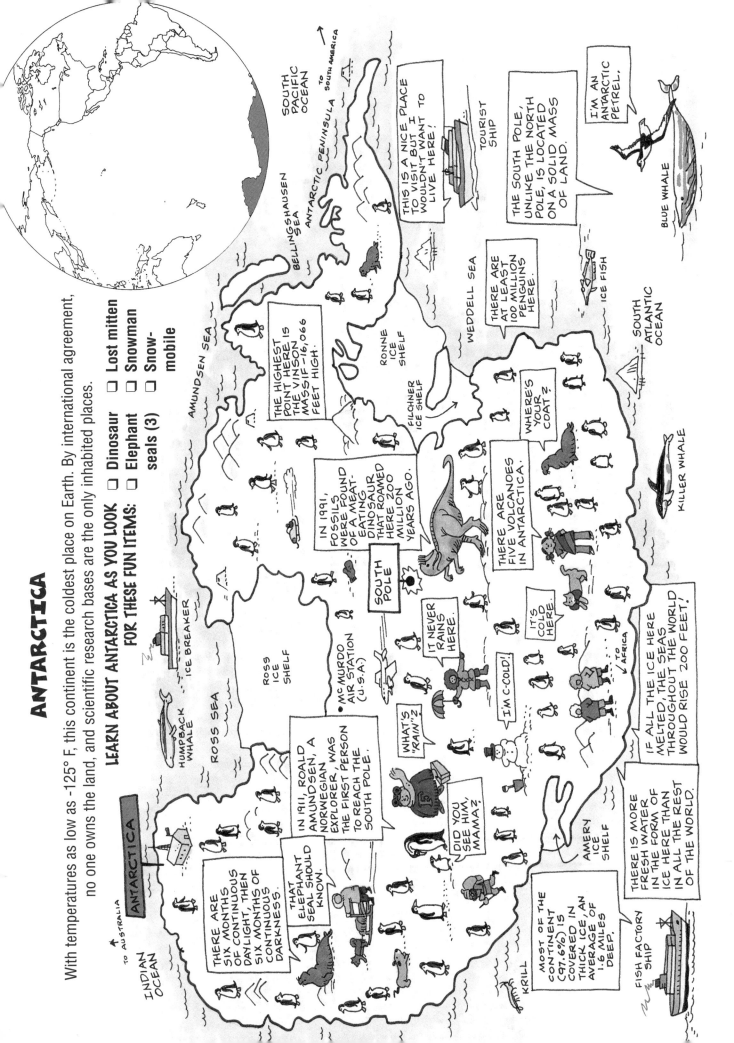

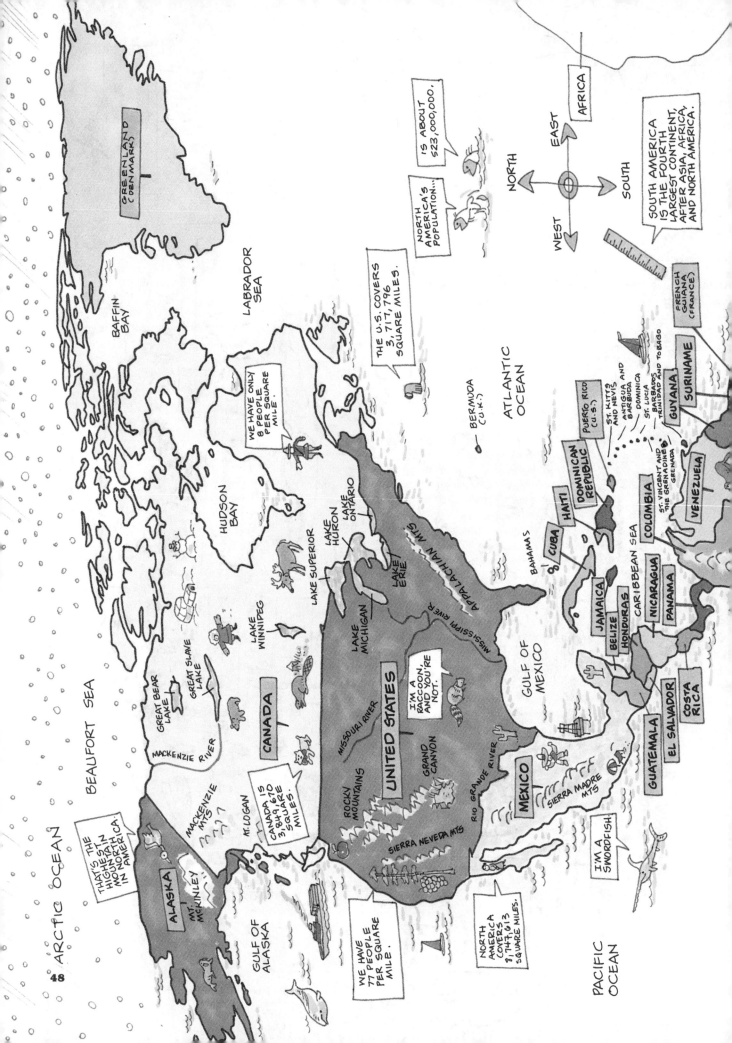

NORTH AMERICA AND SOUTH AMERICA

North America is the third largest of the seven continents. It stretches from Greenland and Canada in the Arctic north to Panama, which is near the equator. Islands in the Caribbean Sea are are also part of North America. South America is the fourth largest continent. From equatorial Colombia, it extends farther south than any continent except Antarctica.

LEARN ABOUT NORTH AND SOUTH AMERICA AS YOU LOOK FOR THESE FUN ITEMS:

- ☐ Banana
- ☐ Cactuses (2)
- ☐ Coffeepot
- ☐ Igloo
- ☐ Monkey
- ☐ Moose
- ☐ Parrot
- ☐ Penguin
- ☐ Periscope
- ☐ Sailboats (2)
- ☐ Shipwreck
- ☐ Snowman
- ☐ Soccer player
- ☐ Surfer
- ☐ Swordfish

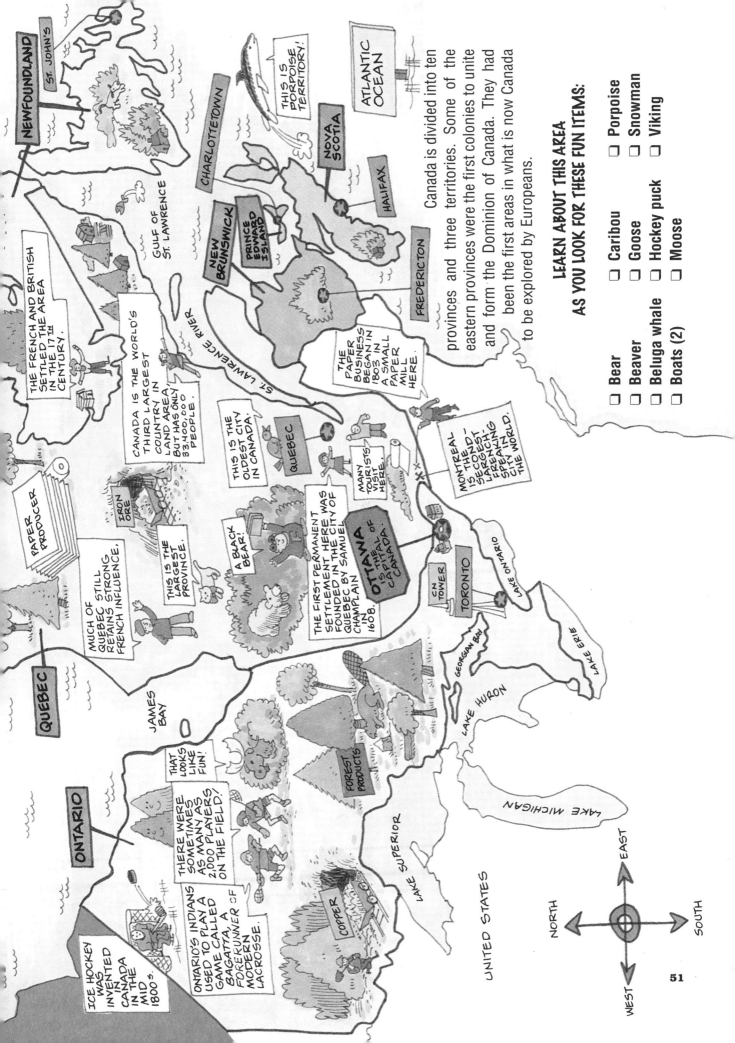

NEWFOUNDLAND

ST. JOHN'S

CHARLOTTETOWN

THIS IS PORPOISE TERRITORY!

NOVA SCOTIA

ATLANTIC OCEAN

HALIFAX

NEW BRUNSWICK

PRINCE EDWARD ISLAND

FREDERICTON

GULF OF ST. LAWRENCE

THE FRENCH AND BRITISH SETTLED THE AREA IN THE 17TH CENTURY.

ST. LAWRENCE RIVER

CANADA IS THE WORLD'S THIRD LARGEST COUNTRY IN LAND AREA BUT HAS ONLY 33,400,000 PEOPLE.

THE PAPER BUSINESS BEGAN IN 1803 IN A SMALL PAPER MILL HERE.

THIS IS THE OLDEST CITY IN CANADA.

QUEBEC

MANY TOURISTS VISIT HERE.

MONTREAL IS THE SECOND-LARGEST FRENCH-SPEAKING CITY IN THE WORLD.

PAPER PRODUCER

IRON ORE

MUCH OF QUEBEC STILL RETAINS STRONG FRENCH INFLUENCE.

THIS IS THE LARGEST PROVINCE.

A BLACK BEAR!

THE FIRST PERMANENT SETTLEMENT HERE WAS FOUNDED IN THE CITY OF QUEBEC BY SAMUEL CHAMPLAIN IN 1608.

OTTAWA IS THE CAPITAL OF CANADA.

CN TOWER

TORONTO

LAKE ONTARIO

LAKE ERIE

QUEBEC

JAMES BAY

ONTARIO

THAT LOOKS LIKE FUN!

THERE WERE SOMETIMES AS MANY AS 2,000 PLAYERS ON THE FIELD!

ONTARIO'S INDIANS USED TO PLAY A GAME CALLED BAGATTA, A FORERUNNER OF MODERN LACROSSE.

ICE HOCKEY WAS INVENTED IN CANADA IN THE MID 1800s.

FOREST PRODUCTS

GEORGIAN BAY

LAKE HURON

LAKE SUPERIOR

COPPER

LAKE MICHIGAN

UNITED STATES

NORTH

EAST

WEST

SOUTH

LEARN ABOUT THIS AREA
AS YOU LOOK FOR THESE FUN ITEMS:

- ☐ Bear
- ☐ Beaver
- ☐ Beluga whale
- ☐ Boats (2)
- ☐ Caribou
- ☐ Goose
- ☐ Hockey puck
- ☐ Moose
- ☐ Porpoise
- ☐ Snowman
- ☐ Viking

Canada is divided into ten provinces and three territories. Some of the eastern provinces were the first colonies to unite and form the Dominion of Canada. They had been the first areas in what is now Canada to be explored by Europeans.

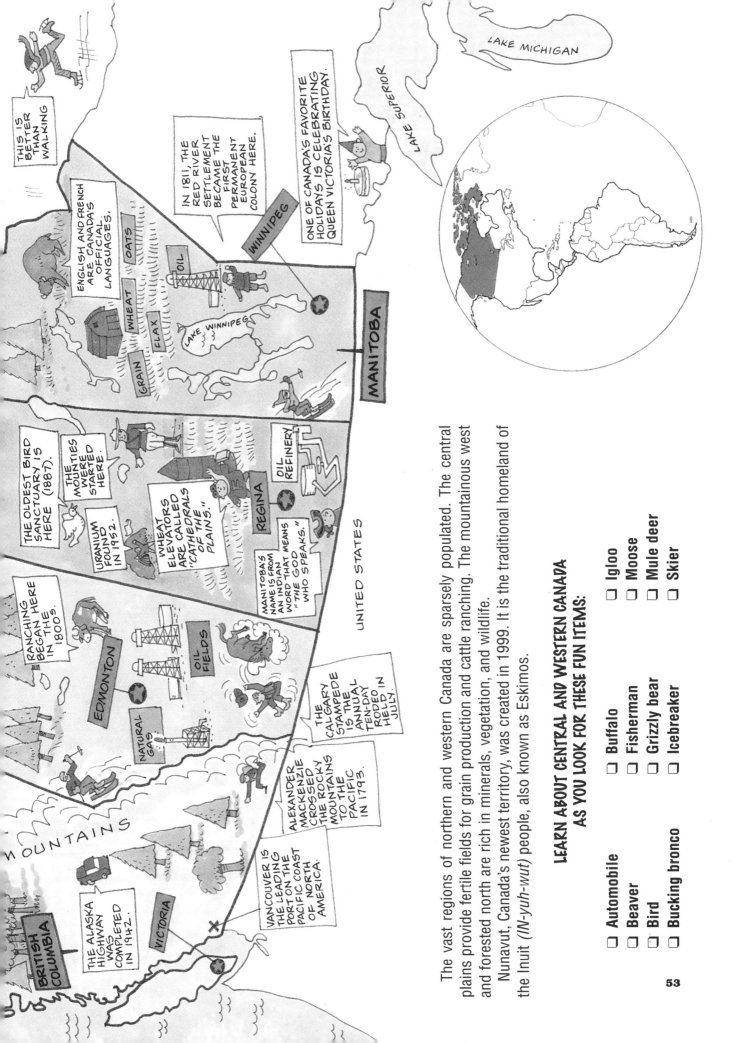

The vast regions of northern and western Canada are sparsely populated. The central plains provide fertile fields for grain production and cattle ranching. The mountainous west and forested north are rich in minerals, vegetation, and wildlife. Nunavut, Canada's newest territory, was created in 1999. It is the traditional homeland of the Inuit (*IN-yuh-wut*) people, also known as Eskimos.

LEARN ABOUT CENTRAL AND WESTERN CANADA AS YOU LOOK FOR THESE FUN ITEMS:

☐ Automobile	☐ Buffalo	☐ Igloo
☐ Beaver	☐ Fisherman	☐ Moose
☐ Bird	☐ Grizzly bear	☐ Mule deer
☐ Bucking bronco	☐ Icebreaker	☐ Skier

THE UNITED STATES OF AMERICA

The United States of America is the world's third-largest country in population (after China and India) and the fourth-largest in land area (after Russia, China, and Canada). Its huge economic, political, and military influence make it the world's leading superpower.

In the 18th century, Britain ruled 13 American colonies. The U.S. became an independent nation in 1776, when it rebelled against British rule. Those colonies became the original 13 states. Today, the U.S. is a nation of 50 states. Washington, D.C., is the national capital and federal district. Outlying territories and other areas include Puerto Rico, the U.S. Virgin Islands, and Guam.

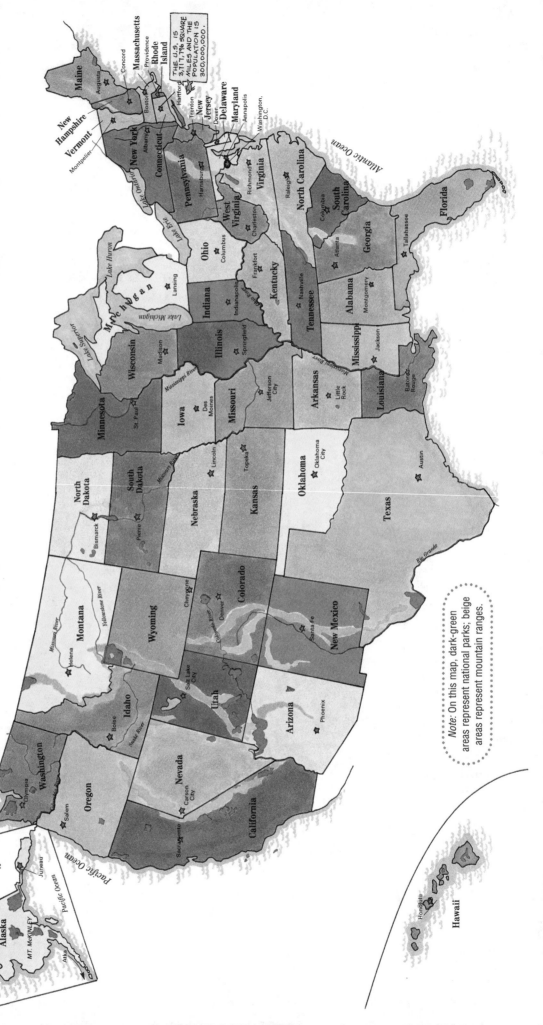

THE U.S. IS 3,717,716 SQUARE MILES AND THE POPULATION IS 300,000,000 .

Note: On this map, dark-green areas represent national parks; beige areas represent mountain ranges.

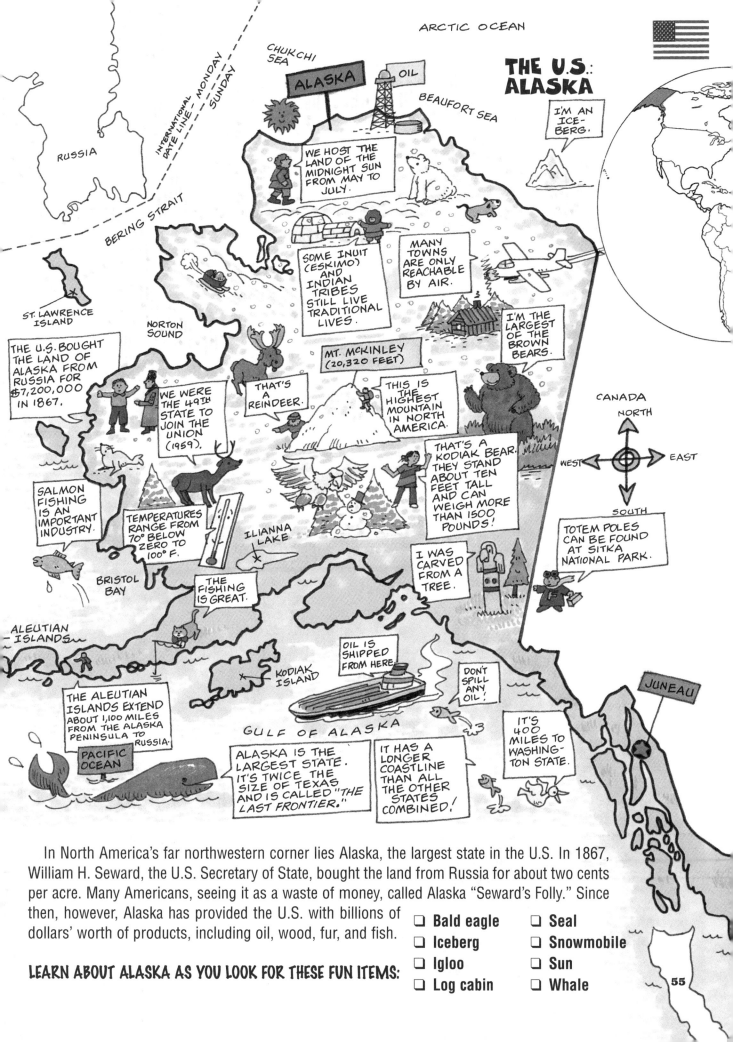

ALASKA

OIL

I'M AN ICE-BERG.

CHUKCHI SEA

BEAUFORT SEA

RUSSIA

BERING STRAIT

WE HOST THE LAND OF THE MIDNIGHT SUN FROM MAY TO JULY.

SOME INUIT (ESKIMO) AND INDIAN TRIBES STILL LIVE TRADITIONAL LIVES.

MANY TOWNS ARE ONLY REACHABLE BY AIR.

I'M THE LARGEST OF THE BROWN BEARS.

ST. LAWRENCE ISLAND

NORTON SOUND

THE U.S. BOUGHT THE LAND OF ALASKA FROM RUSSIA FOR $7,200,000 IN 1867.

WE WERE THE 49TH STATE TO JOIN THE UNION (1959).

THAT'S A REINDEER.

MT. McKINLEY (20,320 FEET)

THIS IS THE HIGHEST MOUNTAIN IN NORTH AMERICA.

THAT'S A KODIAK BEAR. THEY STAND ABOUT TEN FEET TALL AND CAN WEIGH MORE THAN 1500 POUNDS!

CANADA

NORTH

WEST — EAST

SOUTH

SALMON FISHING IS AN IMPORTANT INDUSTRY.

TEMPERATURES RANGE FROM 70° BELOW ZERO TO 100° F.

ILIANNA LAKE

I WAS CARVED FROM A TREE.

TOTEM POLES CAN BE FOUND AT SITKA NATIONAL PARK.

BRISTOL BAY

THE FISHING IS GREAT.

ALEUTIAN ISLANDS

OIL IS SHIPPED FROM HERE.

DON'T SPILL ANY OIL!

IT'S 400 MILES TO WASHINGTON STATE.

JUNEAU

THE ALEUTIAN ISLANDS EXTEND ABOUT 1,100 MILES FROM THE ALASKA PENINSULA TO RUSSIA.

PACIFIC OCEAN

KODIAK ISLAND

GULF OF ALASKA

ALASKA IS THE LARGEST STATE. IT'S TWICE THE SIZE OF TEXAS AND IS CALLED "THE LAST FRONTIER."

IT HAS A LONGER COASTLINE THAN ALL THE OTHER STATES COMBINED!

In North America's far northwestern corner lies Alaska, the largest state in the U.S. In 1867, William H. Seward, the U.S. Secretary of State, bought the land from Russia for about two cents per acre. Many Americans, seeing it as a waste of money, called Alaska "Seward's Folly." Since then, however, Alaska has provided the U.S. with billions of dollars' worth of products, including oil, wood, fur, and fish.

LEARN ABOUT ALASKA AS YOU LOOK FOR THESE FUN ITEMS:

- ❏ Bald eagle
- ❏ Iceberg
- ❏ Igloo
- ❏ Log cabin
- ❏ Seal
- ❏ Snowmobile
- ❏ Sun
- ❏ Whale

THE U.S.: THE WESTERN STATES

The western part of the country is characterized by deserts, mountains, river canyons, and great forests. Separated from the rest of the continental U.S. by the Rocky Mountains, parts of this area—especially along the coast—were rapidly settled and developed after railroads were built in the mid-19th century, linking west to east. The Hawaiian Islands became a U.S. territory in 1900 and the 50th state in 1959.

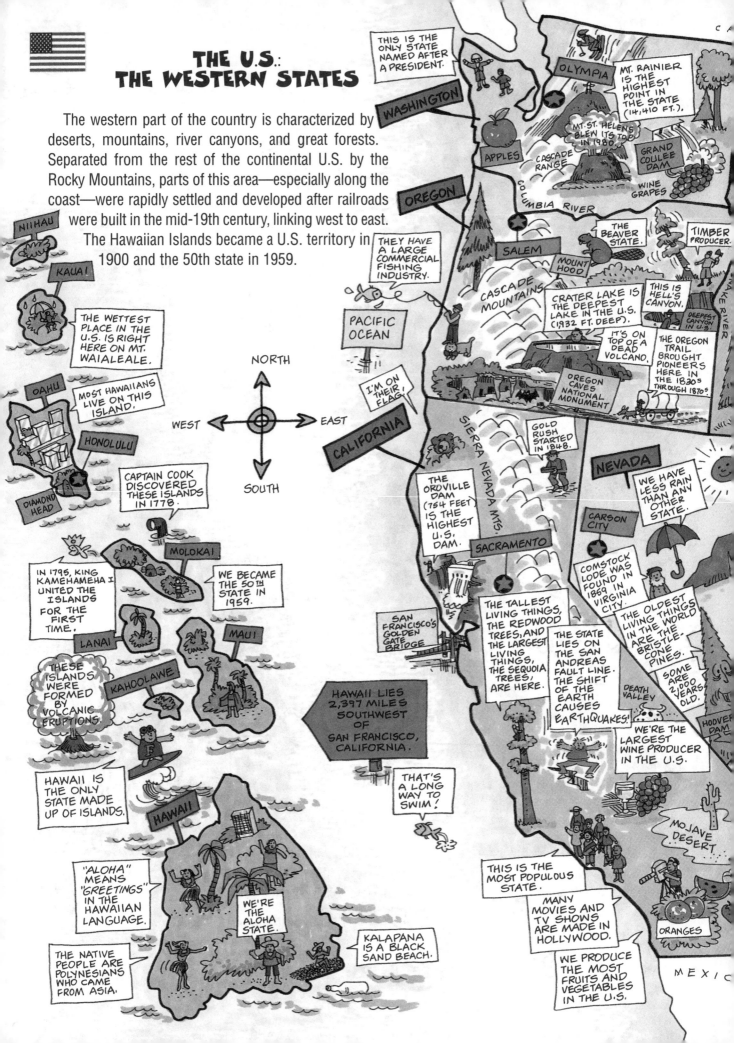

THIS IS THE ONLY STATE NAMED AFTER A PRESIDENT.

OLYMPIA

WASHINGTON

MT. RAINIER IS THE HIGHEST POINT IN THE STATE (14,410 FT.).

MT. ST. HELENS BLEW ITS TOP IN 1980.

GRAND COULEE DAM

APPLES

CASCADE RANGE

WINE GRAPES

OREGON

COLUMBIA RIVER

THE BEAVER STATE.

TIMBER PRODUCER.

NIIHAU

KAUAI

SALEM

MOUNT HOOD

THEY HAVE A LARGE COMMERCIAL FISHING INDUSTRY.

CASCADE MOUNTAINS

CRATER LAKE IS THE DEEPEST LAKE IN THE U.S. (1,932 FT. DEEP).

THIS IS HELL'S CANYON.

DEEPEST CANYON IN U.S.

THE WETTEST PLACE IN THE U.S. IS RIGHT HERE ON MT. WAIALEALE.

PACIFIC OCEAN

IT'S ON TOP OF A DEAD VOLCANO.

THE OREGON TRAIL BROUGHT PIONEERS HERE IN THE 1830s THROUGH 1870s.

OAHU

MOST HAWAIIANS LIVE ON THIS ISLAND.

NORTH

I'M ON THEIR FLAG!

OREGON CAVES NATIONAL MONUMENT

WEST — EAST

CALIFORNIA

SIERRA NEVADA MTS.

GOLD RUSH STARTED IN 1848.

NEVADA

WE HAVE LESS RAIN THAN ANY OTHER STATE.

HONOLULU

SOUTH

THE OROVILLE DAM (754 FEET) IS THE HIGHEST U.S. DAM.

CARSON CITY

DIAMOND HEAD

CAPTAIN COOK DISCOVERED THESE ISLANDS IN 1778.

SACRAMENTO

COMSTOCK LODE WAS FOUND IN 1869 IN VIRGINIA CITY.

THE OLDEST LIVING THINGS IN THE WORLD ARE THE BRISTLE-CONE PINES.

MOLOKAI

IN 1795, KING KAMEHAMEHA I UNITED THE ISLANDS FOR THE FIRST TIME.

WE BECAME THE 50TH STATE IN 1959.

SAN FRANCISCO'S GOLDEN GATE BRIDGE

THE TALLEST LIVING THINGS, THE REDWOOD TREES, AND THE LARGEST LIVING THINGS, THE SEQUOIA TREES, ARE HERE.

THE STATE LIES ON THE SAN ANDREAS FAULT LINE. THE SHIFT OF THE EARTH CAUSES EARTHQUAKES!

DEATH VALLEY

SOME ARE 2,000 YEARS OLD.

HOOVER DAM

LANAI

MAUI

THESE ISLANDS WERE FORMED BY VOLCANIC ERUPTIONS.

KAHOOLAWE

HAWAII LIES 2,397 MILES SOUTHWEST OF SAN FRANCISCO, CALIFORNIA.

WE'RE THE LARGEST WINE PRODUCER IN THE U.S.

HAWAII IS THE ONLY STATE MADE UP OF ISLANDS.

THAT'S A LONG WAY TO SWIM!

MOJAVE DESERT

HAWAII

"ALOHA" MEANS "GREETINGS" IN THE HAWAIIAN LANGUAGE.

WE'RE THE ALOHA STATE.

THIS IS THE MOST POPULOUS STATE.

MANY MOVIES AND TV SHOWS ARE MADE IN HOLLYWOOD.

ORANGES

THE NATIVE PEOPLE ARE POLYNESIANS WHO CAME FROM ASIA.

KALAPANA IS A BLACK SAND BEACH.

WE PRODUCE THE MOST FRUITS AND VEGETABLES IN THE U.S.

MEXICO

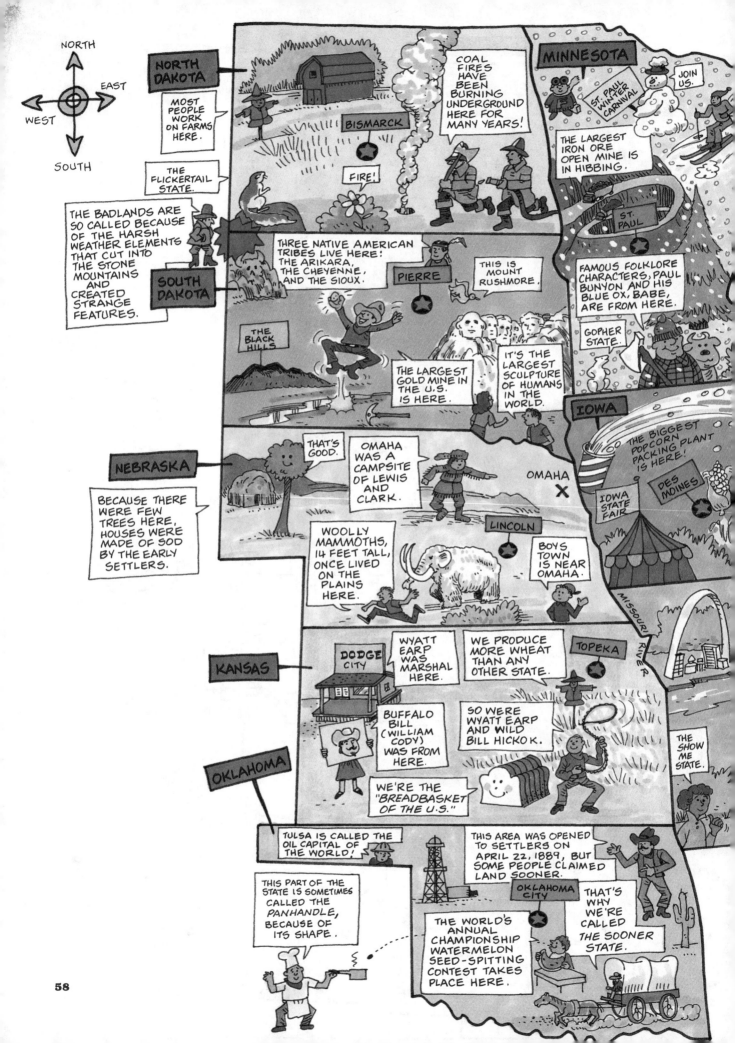

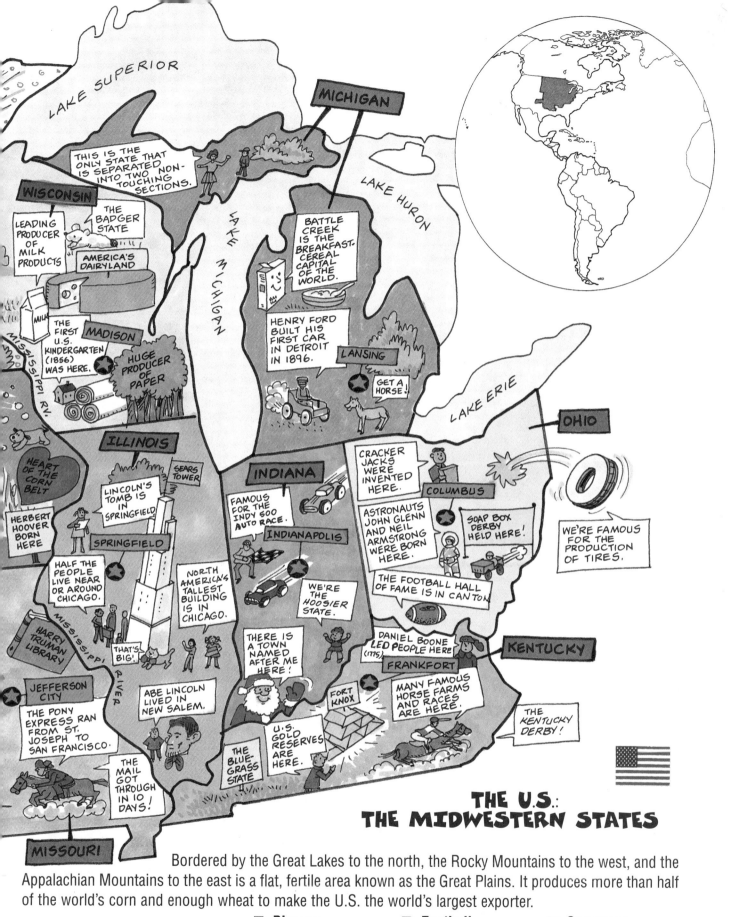

THE U.S.: THE MIDWESTERN STATES

Bordered by the Great Lakes to the north, the Rocky Mountains to the west, and the Appalachian Mountains to the east is a flat, fertile area known as the Great Plains. It produces more than half of the world's corn and enough wheat to make the U.S. the world's largest exporter.

LEARN ABOUT THE U.S.A.'S MIDWESTERN STATES AS YOU LOOK FOR THESE FUN ITEMS:

- ❑ Blue ox
- ❑ Book
- ❑ Cereal
- ❑ Flower
- ❑ Football
- ❑ Heart
- ❑ Race cars (3)
- ❑ Santa Claus
- ❑ Snowman
- ❑ Tire
- ❑ Watermelon slice
- ❑ Woolly mammoth

THE U.S.: THE NORTHEASTERN AND MIDATLANTIC STATES

The most populous region in the country, the northeast and midatlantic states were the first to be settled by Europeans. Colonists arrived from England in 1620 and settled in New Plymouth, Massachusetts.

LEARN ABOUT U.S.A.'S NORTHEASTERN AND MIDATLANTIC STATES AS YOU LOOK FOR THESE FUN ITEMS:

- ❑ Anchor
- ❑ Apple
- ❑ Baseball
- ❑ Basketball
- ❑ Cannon

- ❑ Kite
- ❑ Lighthouse
- ❑ Lobster
- ❑ Ship
- ❑ Skier

- ❑ Treasure chest
- ❑ Truck
- ❑ Umbrella

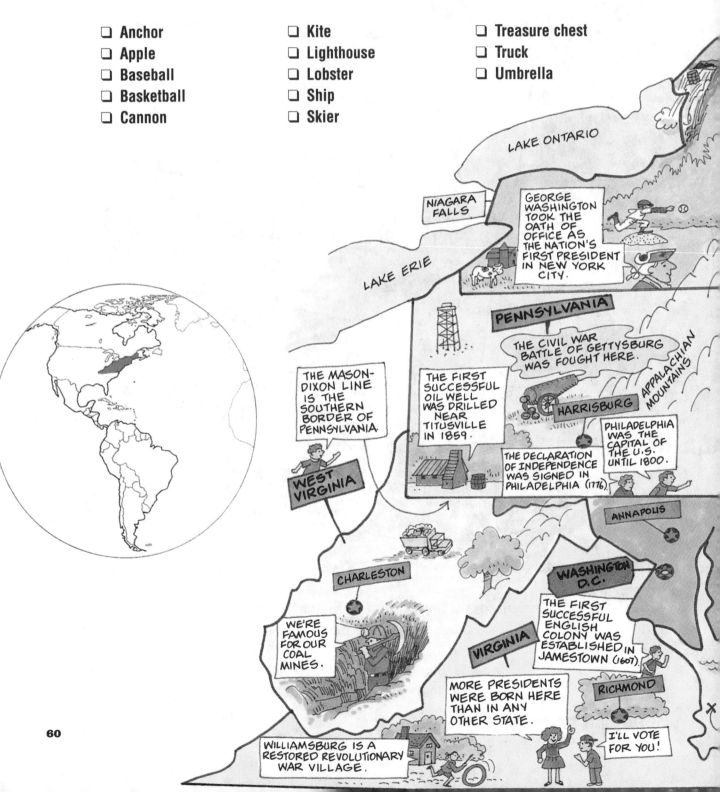

LAKE ONTARIO

NIAGARA FALLS

GEORGE WASHINGTON TOOK THE OATH OF OFFICE AS THE NATION'S FIRST PRESIDENT IN NEW YORK CITY.

LAKE ERIE

PENNSYLVANIA

THE CIVIL WAR BATTLE OF GETTYSBURG WAS FOUGHT HERE.

THE MASON-DIXON LINE IS THE SOUTHERN BORDER OF PENNSYLVANIA.

THE FIRST SUCCESSFUL OIL WELL WAS DRILLED NEAR TITUSVILLE IN 1859.

APPALACHIAN MOUNTAINS

HARRISBURG

PHILADELPHIA WAS THE CAPITAL OF THE U.S. UNTIL 1800.

THE DECLARATION OF INDEPENDENCE WAS SIGNED IN PHILADELPHIA (1776).

WEST VIRGINIA

ANNAPOLIS

CHARLESTON

WASHINGTON D.C.

THE FIRST SUCCESSFUL ENGLISH COLONY WAS ESTABLISHED IN JAMESTOWN (1607).

WE'RE FAMOUS FOR OUR COAL MINES.

VIRGINIA

RICHMOND

MORE PRESIDENTS WERE BORN HERE THAN IN ANY OTHER STATE.

I'LL VOTE FOR YOU!

WILLIAMSBURG IS A RESTORED REVOLUTIONARY WAR VILLAGE.

THE U.S.: THE SOUTHERN STATES

The southern states, which extend from the Atlantic coast to Texas, were once totally farm based, producing mainly cotton and tobacco. Although still agricultural, the area is now strong in industry, and produces oil as well as iron and steel.

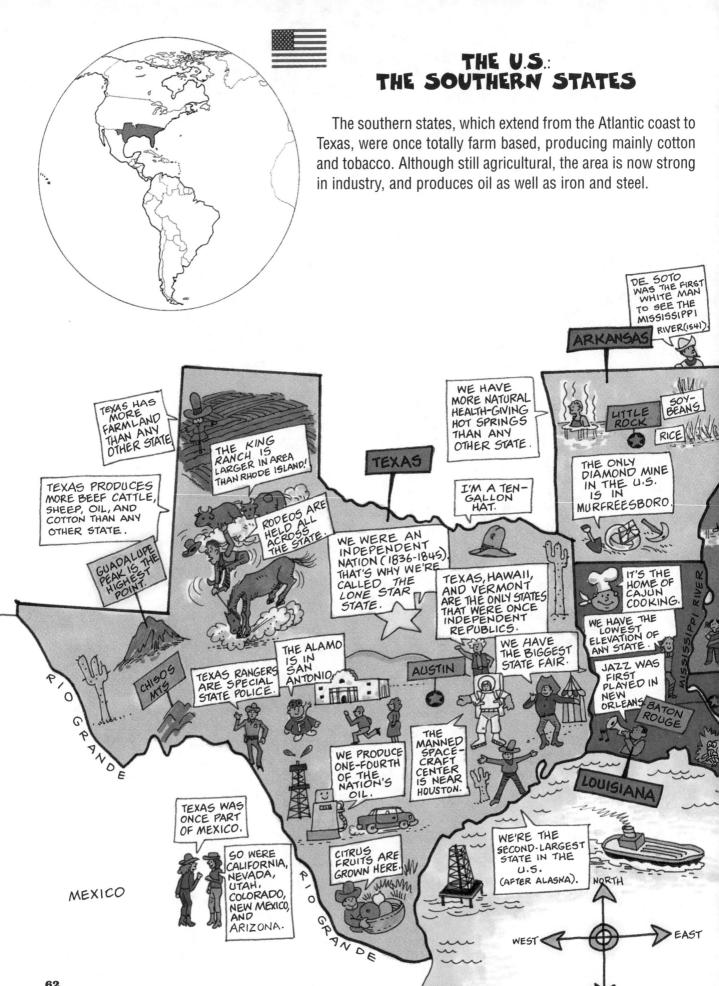

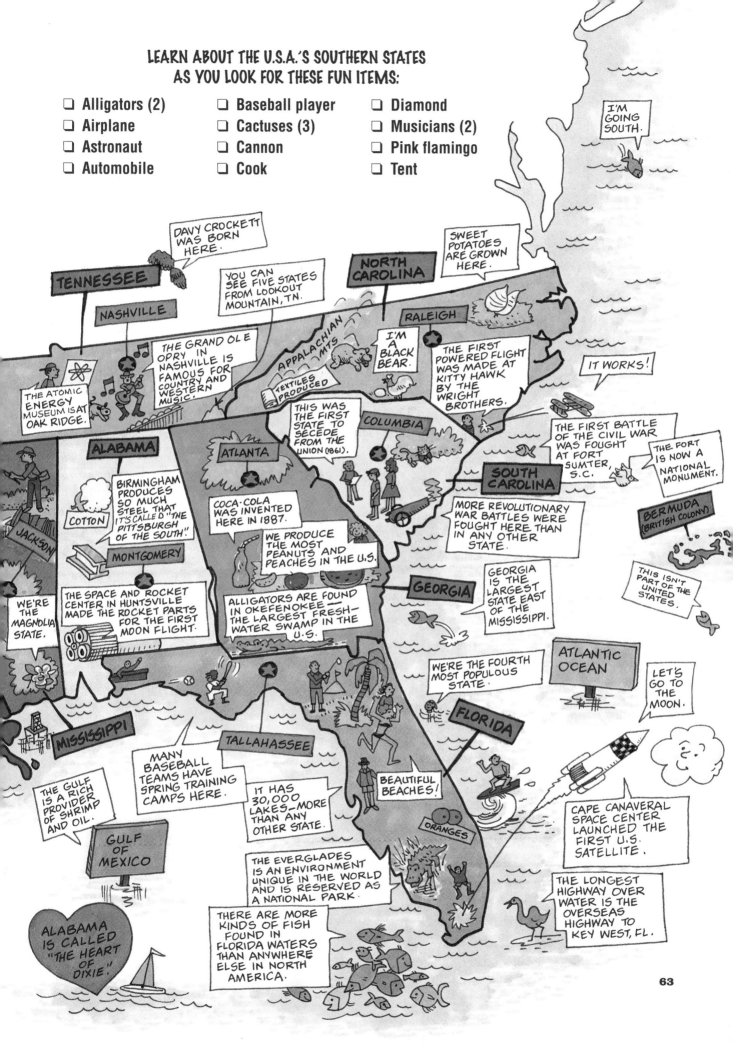

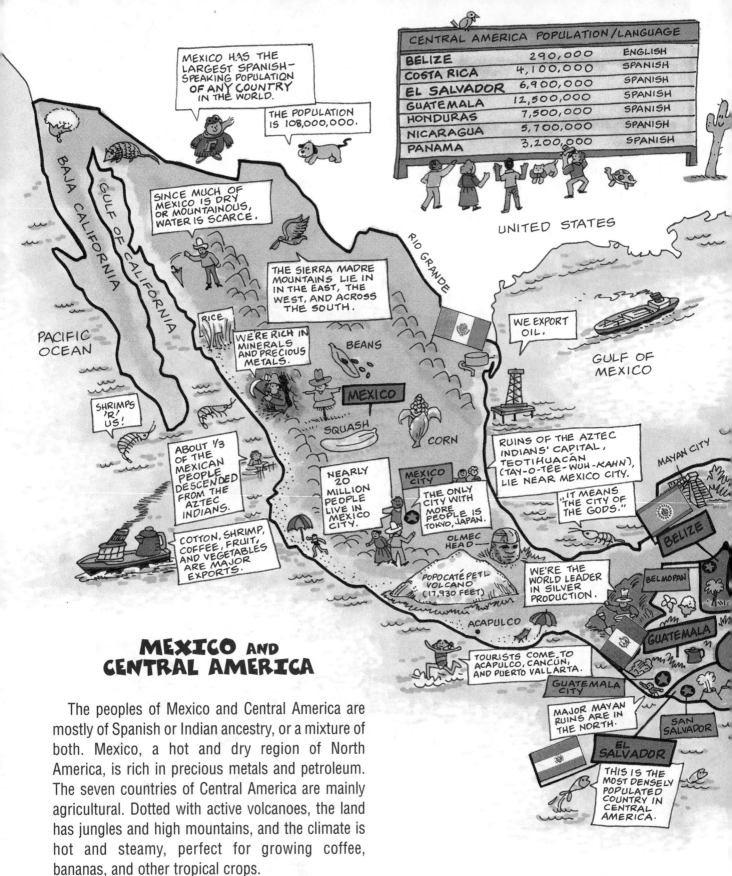

CENTRAL AMERICA POPULATION/LANGUAGE		
BELIZE	290,000	ENGLISH
COSTA RICA	4,100,000	SPANISH
EL SALVADOR	6,900,000	SPANISH
GUATEMALA	12,500,000	SPANISH
HONDURAS	7,500,000	SPANISH
NICARAGUA	5,700,000	SPANISH
PANAMA	3,200,000	SPANISH

MEXICO AND CENTRAL AMERICA

The peoples of Mexico and Central America are mostly of Spanish or Indian ancestry, or a mixture of both. Mexico, a hot and dry region of North America, is rich in precious metals and petroleum. The seven countries of Central America are mainly agricultural. Dotted with active volcanoes, the land has jungles and high mountains, and the climate is hot and steamy, perfect for growing coffee, bananas, and other tropical crops.

LEARN ABOUT MEXICO, CENTRAL AMERICA, AND THE CARIBBEAN NATIONS AS YOU LOOK FOR THESE FUN ITEMS:

- ❑ Armadillo
- ❑ Coffeepots (3)
- ❑ Cotton (3)
- ❑ Diver
- ❑ Miner
- ❑ Oil well
- ❑ Photographer
- ❑ Pineapple
- ❑ Sailor
- ❑ Scarecrow
- ❑ Shovel
- ❑ Shrimp (3)
- ❑ Squash
- ❑ Turtle
- ❑ Umbrellas (3)

THE CARIBBEAN NATIONS

A chain of tropical islands about 2,000 miles long stretches across the Caribbean Sea, then curves like a hook toward South America. These islands were the first land in the Americas that Christopher Columbus saw and set foot on during his 1492 voyage of discovery. In the 16th century, Europeans colonized the islands, bringing African slaves to work plantations.

Today, 13 of the islands or island groups are independent nations (see list below). Others are territories of the U.S. or European countries. Most of the people living here are descendants of African slaves, Spanish conquerors, or both. Most countries in this region depend on tourism and agriculture for their income.

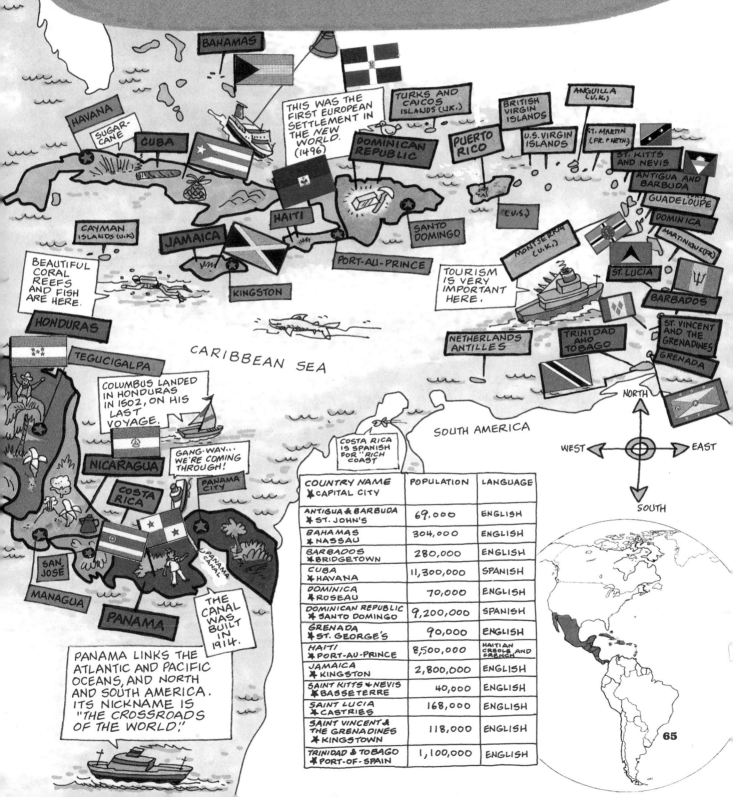

COUNTRY NAME ✱CAPITAL CITY	POPULATION	LANGUAGE
ANTIGUA & BARBUDA ✱ST. JOHN'S	69,000	ENGLISH
BAHAMAS ✱NASSAU	304,000	ENGLISH
BARBADOS ✱BRIDGETOWN	280,000	ENGLISH
CUBA ✱HAVANA	11,300,000	SPANISH
DOMINICA ✱ROSEAU	70,000	ENGLISH
DOMINICAN REPUBLIC ✱SANTO DOMINGO	9,200,000	SPANISH
GRENADA ✱ST. GEORGE'S	90,000	ENGLISH
HAITI ✱PORT-AU-PRINCE	8,500,000	HAITIAN CREOLE AND FRENCH
JAMAICA ✱KINGSTON	2,800,000	ENGLISH
SAINT KITTS & NEVIS ✱BASSETERRE	40,000	ENGLISH
SAINT LUCIA ✱CASTRIES	168,000	ENGLISH
SAINT VINCENT & THE GRENADINES ✱KINGSTOWN	118,000	ENGLISH
TRINIDAD & TOBAGO ✱PORT-OF-SPAIN	1,100,000	ENGLISH

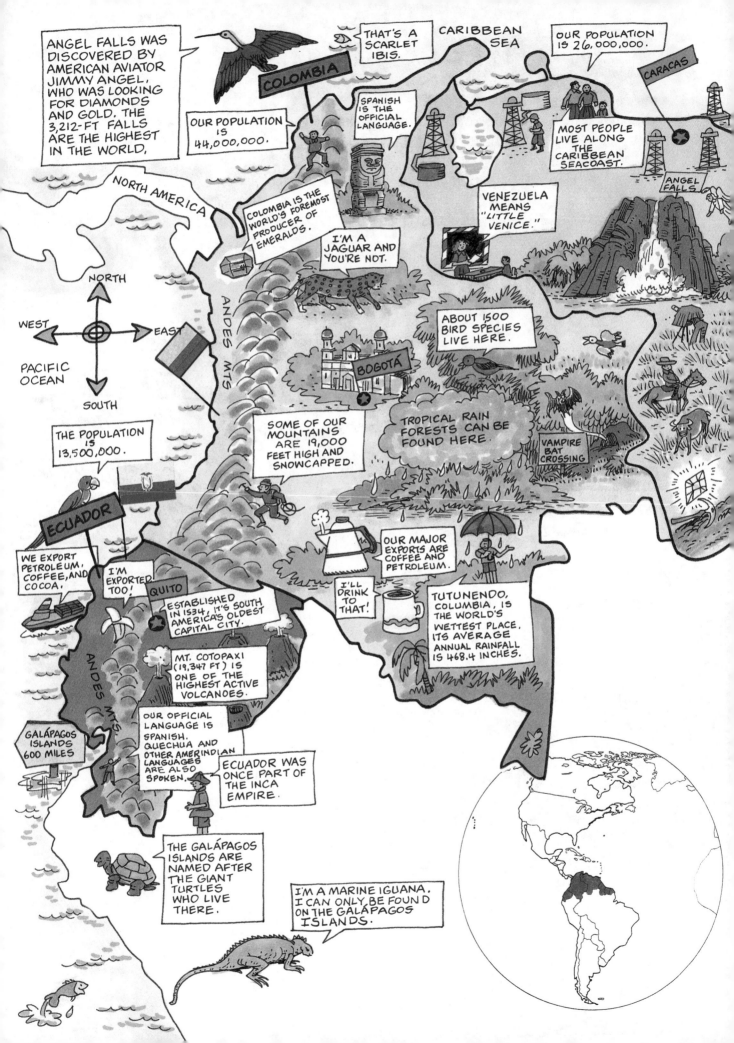

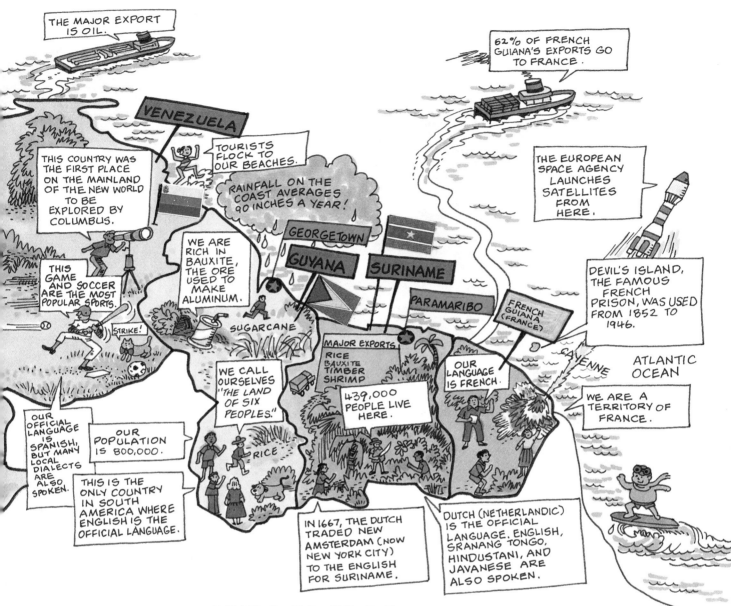

SOUTH AMERICA:
THE NORTHERN NATIONS

The northern part of South America is dominated by the Andes mountain range in the west, and by the Amazon forest. The people, like the rest of South America, are of European, Indian, and mixed ancestry.

Once Spanish colonies, Ecuador, Colombia, and Venezuela won their independence in the early decades of the 19th century. Guyana and Suriname gained their independence only recently: Guyana in 1966, from Britain; and Suriname in 1975, from the Netherlands. French Guiana is the only country on the South American mainland that is still a European territory.

LEARN ABOUT SOUTH AMERICA'S NORTHERN NATIONS
AS YOU LOOK FOR THESE FUN ITEMS:

- ❏ Aluminum can
- ❏ Angel
- ❏ Baseball bat
- ❏ Cup
- ❏ Emerald
- ❏ Flying bat
- ❏ Ibis
- ❏ Iguana
- ❏ Jaguar
- ❏ Mountain climber
- ❏ Photographer
- ❏ Satellite rocket
- ❏ Schoolteacher
- ❏ Soccer ball
- ❏ Stone idol
- ❏ Surfer
- ❏ Telescope
- ❏ Turtle

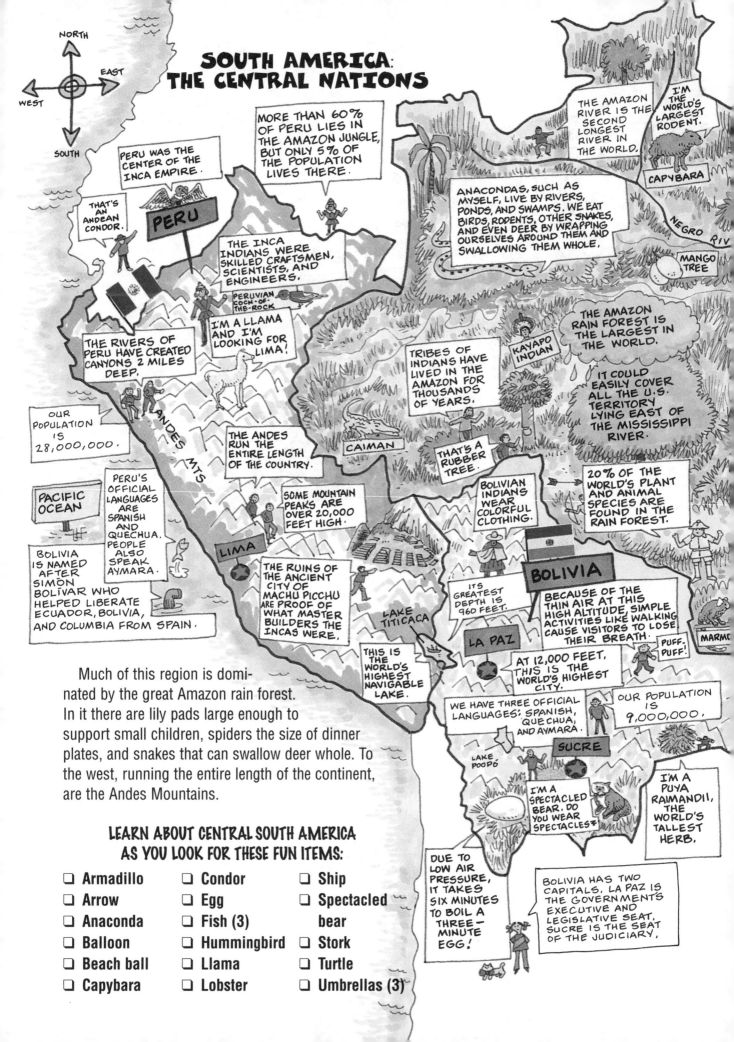

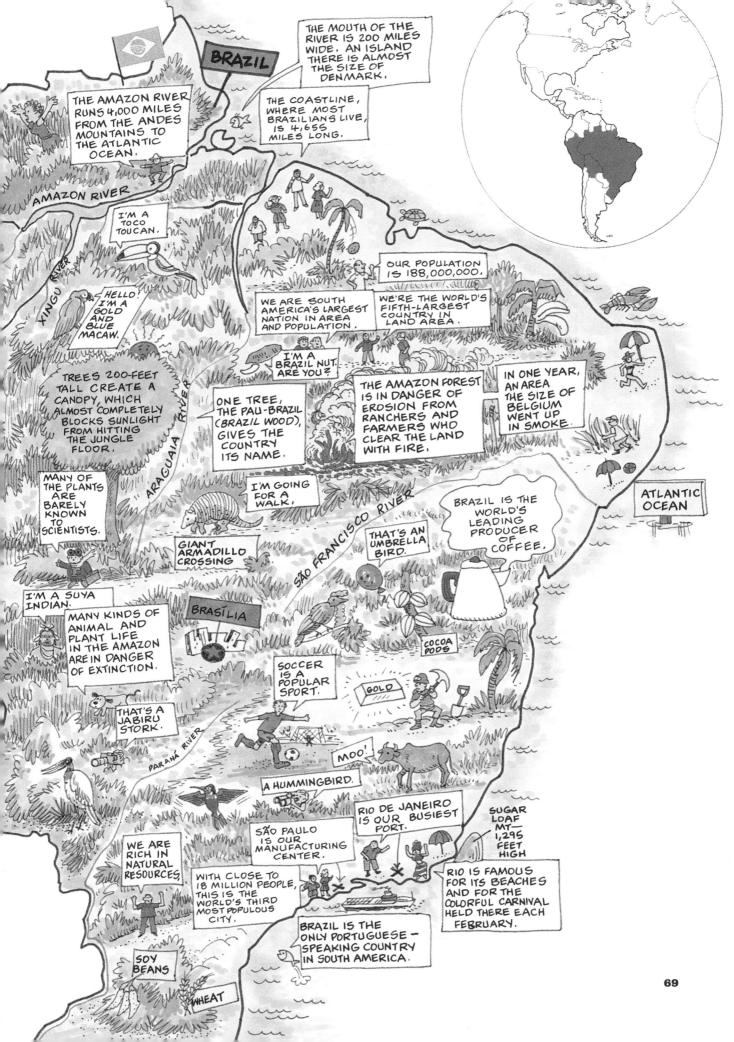

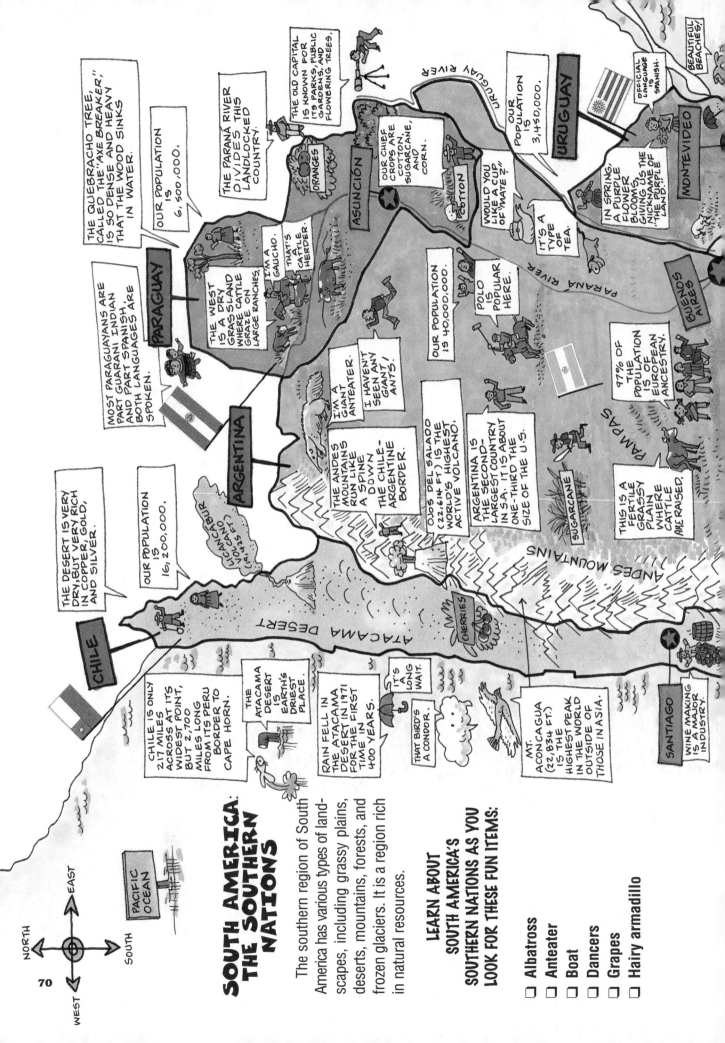

SOUTH AMERICA: THE SOUTHERN NATIONS

The southern region of South America has various types of landscapes, including grassy plains, deserts, mountains, forests, and frozen glaciers. It is a region rich in natural resources.

LEARN ABOUT SOUTH AMERICA'S SOUTHERN NATIONS AS YOU LOOK FOR THESE FUN ITEMS:

- ☐ Albatross
- ☐ Anteater
- ☐ Boat
- ☐ Dancers
- ☐ Grapes
- ☐ Hairy armadillo

70

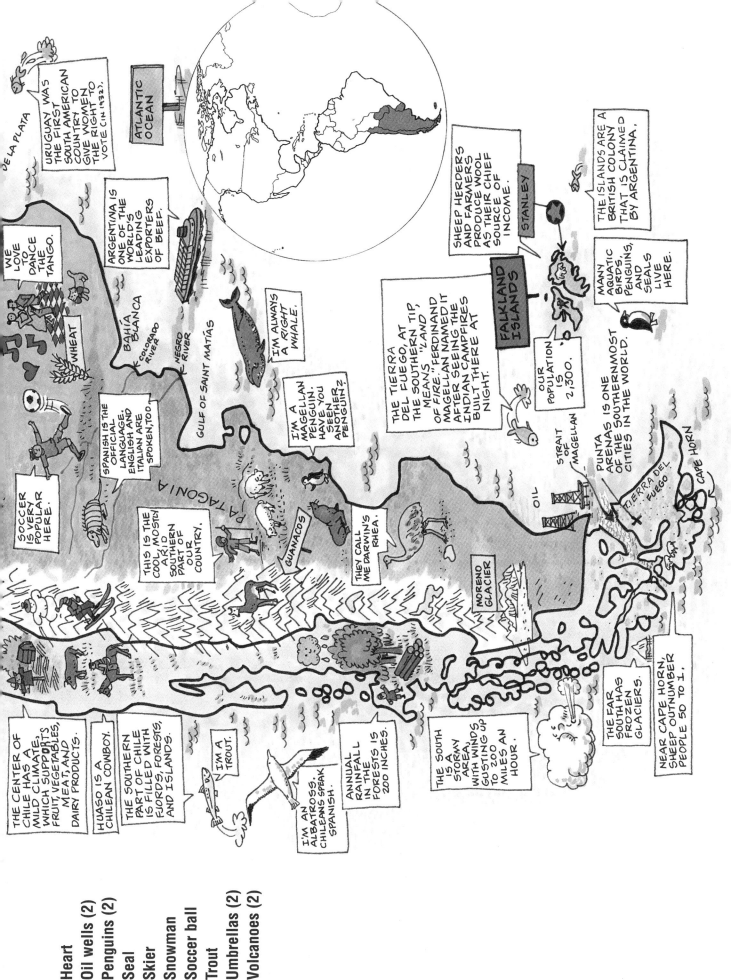

EUROPE

The seat of Western civilization, Europe has had a strong influence on the world through trade, exploration, and industry.

The continent stretches from the icy Arctic Circle in the north to the warm Mediterranean Sea in the south. Its western border is the North Atlantic Ocean and its eastern borders are the Ural and Caucasus mountains. The land—with its fertile plains and tall mountains—is as varied as its countries, peoples, and cultures.

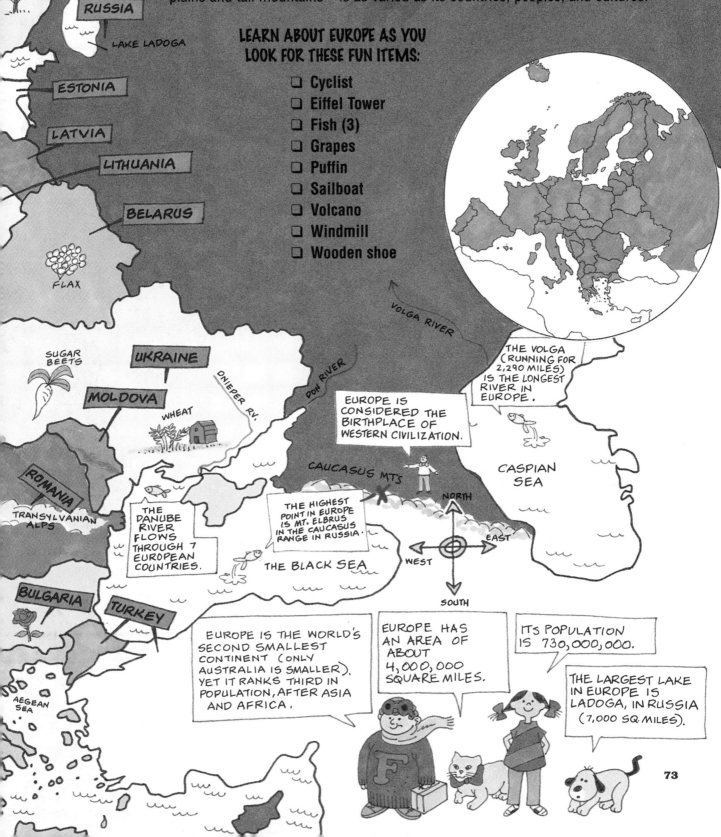

LEARN ABOUT EUROPE AS YOU LOOK FOR THESE FUN ITEMS:

- ❑ Cyclist
- ❑ Eiffel Tower
- ❑ Fish (3)
- ❑ Grapes
- ❑ Puffin
- ❑ Sailboat
- ❑ Volcano
- ❑ Windmill
- ❑ Wooden shoe

FINLAND

RUSSIA

LAKE LADOGA

ESTONIA

LATVIA

LITHUANIA

BELARUS

FLAX

SUGAR BEETS

UKRAINE

MOLDOVA

WHEAT

DNIEPER RV.

DON RIVER

VOLGA RIVER

THE VOLGA (RUNNING FOR 2,290 MILES) IS THE LONGEST RIVER IN EUROPE.

EUROPE IS CONSIDERED THE BIRTHPLACE OF WESTERN CIVILIZATION.

CASPIAN SEA

ROMANIA

TRANSYLVANIAN ALPS

THE DANUBE RIVER FLOWS THROUGH 7 EUROPEAN COUNTRIES.

CAUCASUS MTS

THE HIGHEST POINT IN EUROPE IS MT. ELBRUS IN THE CAUCASUS RANGE IN RUSSIA.

THE BLACK SEA

NORTH

WEST

EAST

SOUTH

BULGARIA

TURKEY

AEGEAN SEA

EUROPE IS THE WORLD'S SECOND SMALLEST CONTINENT (ONLY AUSTRALIA IS SMALLER). YET IT RANKS THIRD IN POPULATION, AFTER ASIA AND AFRICA.

EUROPE HAS AN AREA OF ABOUT 4,000,000 SQUARE MILES.

ITS POPULATION IS 730,000,000.

THE LARGEST LAKE IN EUROPE IS LADOGA, IN RUSSIA (7,000 SQ. MILES).

73

UNITED KINGDOM AND IRELAND

The United Kingdom is a country made up of four parts: England, Wales, Scotland, and Northern Ireland. (The first three are also known as Britain.) Northern Ireland is on the same large island as the independent country of Ireland. In the late 19th and early 20th centuries, Great Britain was the world's leading industrial and trading nation. Its worldwide empire included Canada, India, Australia, New Zealand, and parts of Africa.

LEARN ABOUT THE UNITED KINGDOM AND IRELAND AS YOU LOOK FOR THESE FUN ITEMS:

- ☐ Bagpipe
- ☐ Big Ben
- ☐ Bus
- ☐ Deer
- ☐ Ferry
- ☐ Four-leaf clover
- ☐ Golfer
- ☐ Knight in armor
- ☐ Lobster
- ☐ "Nessie"
- ☐ Potatoes
- ☐ Soccer ball
- ☐ Tennis racket

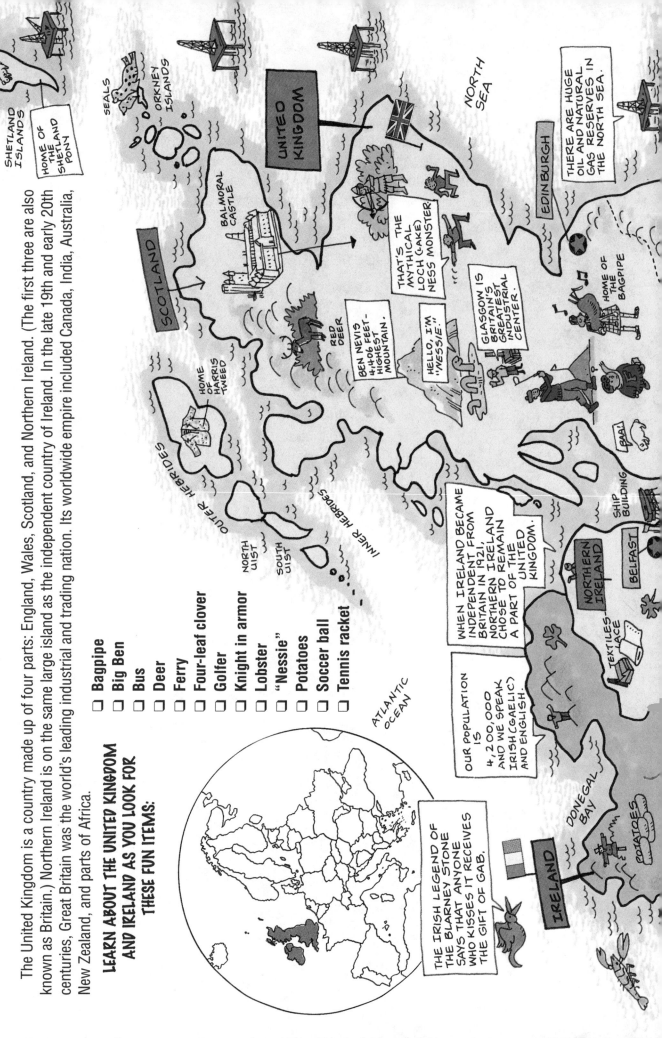

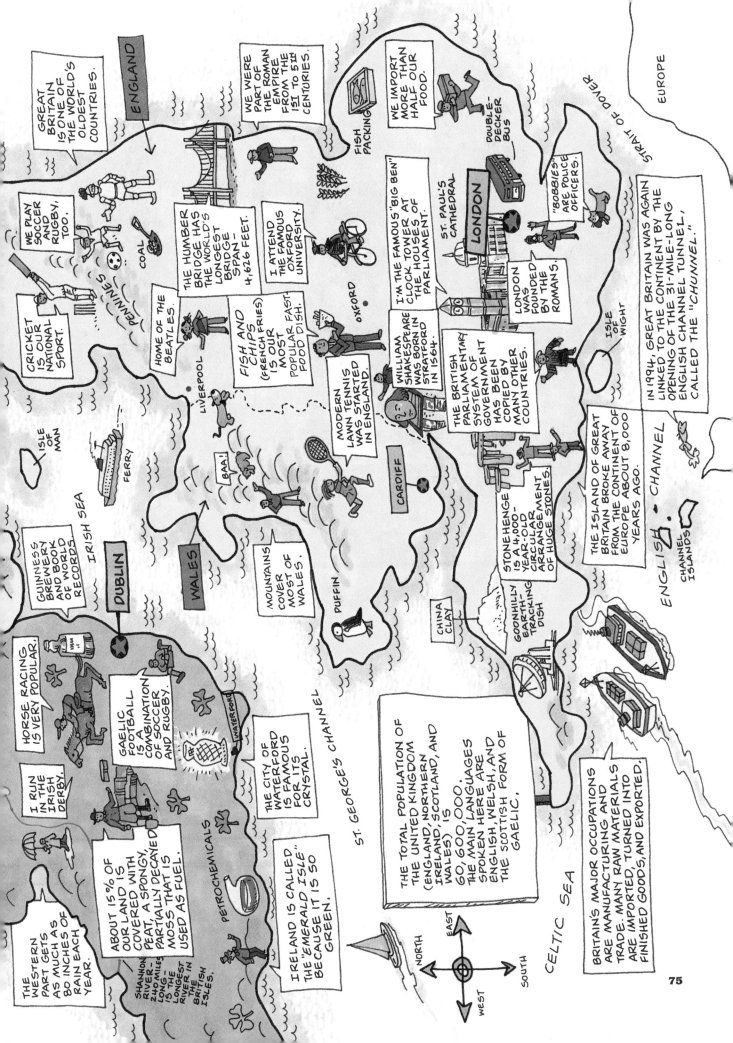

ENGLAND

GREAT BRITAIN IS ONE OF THE WORLD'S OLDEST COUNTRIES.

WE WERE PART OF THE ROMAN EMPIRE FROM THE 1ST TO 5TH CENTURIES.

WE IMPORT MORE THAN HALF OUR FOOD.

FISH PACKING

DOUBLE-DECKER BUS

"BOBBIES" ARE POLICE OFFICERS.

LONDON

ST. PAUL'S CATHEDRAL.

I'M THE FAMOUS "BIG BEN" CLOCK TOWER AT THE HOUSES OF PARLIAMENT.

LONDON WAS FOUNDED BY THE ROMANS.

WE PLAY SOCCER AND RUGBY, TOO.

COAL

THE HUMBER BRIDGE HAS THE WORLD'S LONGEST BRIDGE SPAN— 4,626 FEET.

HOME OF THE BEATLES.

I ATTEND THE FAMOUS OXFORD UNIVERSITY.

OXFORD

CRICKET IS OUR NATIONAL SPORT.

(PENNINES)

FISH AND CHIPS (FRENCH FRIES) IS OUR MOST POPULAR FAST-FOOD DISH.

MODERN LAWN TENNIS WAS STARTED IN ENGLAND.

WILLIAM SHAKESPEARE WAS BORN IN STRATFORD IN 1564.

THE BRITISH PARLIAMENTARY SYSTEM OF GOVERNMENT HAS BEEN COPIED BY MANY OTHER COUNTRIES.

LIVERPOOL

BAA!

IN 1994, GREAT BRITAIN WAS AGAIN LINKED TO THE CONTINENT BY THE OPENING OF THE 31-MILE-LONG ENGLISH CHANNEL TUNNEL, CALLED THE "CHUNNEL."

ISLE OF MAN

FERRY

IRISH SEA

GUINNESS BREWERY AND BOOK OF WORLD RECORDS.

DUBLIN

WALES

MOUNTAINS COVER MOST OF WALES.

PUFFIN

CARDIFF

STONEHENGE IS A 4,000-YEAR-OLD CIRCULAR ARRANGEMENT OF HUGE STONES.

THE ISLAND OF GREAT BRITAIN BROKE AWAY FROM THE CONTINENT OF EUROPE ABOUT 8,000 YEARS AGO.

ISLE OF WIGHT

CHINA CLAY

GOONHILLY EARTH-TRACKING DISH

ENGLISH CHANNEL

CHANNEL ISLANDS

STRAIT OF DOVER

EUROPE

HORSE RACING IS VERY POPULAR.

I RUN IN THE IRISH DERBY.

GAELIC FOOTBALL IS A COMBINATION OF SOCCER AND RUGBY.

WATERFORD

THE CITY OF WATERFORD IS FAMOUS FOR ITS CRYSTAL.

ST. GEORGE'S CHANNEL

THE WESTERN PART GETS AS MUCH AS 80 INCHES OF RAIN EACH YEAR.

ABOUT 15% OF OUR LAND IS COVERED WITH PEAT, A SPONGY, PARTIALLY DECAYED MOSS THAT IS USED AS FUEL.

SHANNON RIVER— 240 MILES LONG—IS THE LONGEST RIVER IN THE BRITISH ISLES.

PETROCHEMICALS

IRELAND IS CALLED THE "EMERALD ISLE" BECAUSE IT IS SO GREEN.

THE TOTAL POPULATION OF THE UNITED KINGDOM (ENGLAND, NORTHERN IRELAND, SCOTLAND, AND WALES) IS 60,600,000. THE MAIN LANGUAGES SPOKEN HERE ARE ENGLISH, WELSH, AND THE SCOTTISH FORM OF GAELIC.

BRITAIN'S MAJOR OCCUPATIONS ARE MANUFACTURING AND TRADE. MANY RAW MATERIALS ARE IMPORTED, TURNED INTO FINISHED GOODS, AND EXPORTED.

CELTIC SEA

NORTH
EAST
SOUTH
WEST

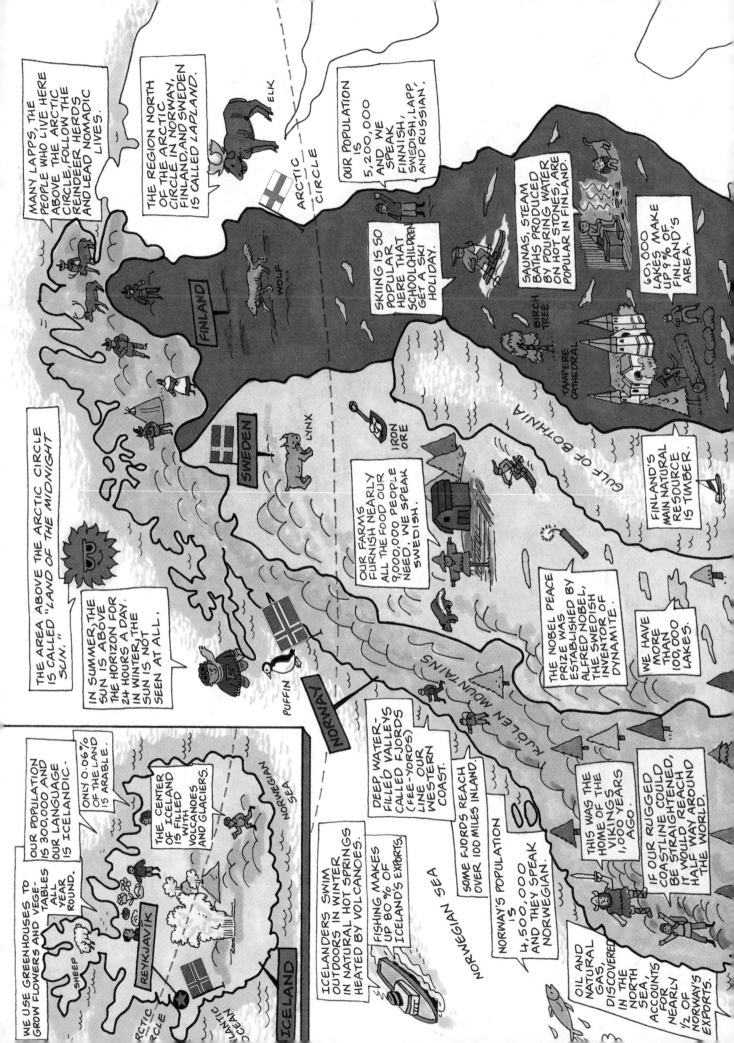

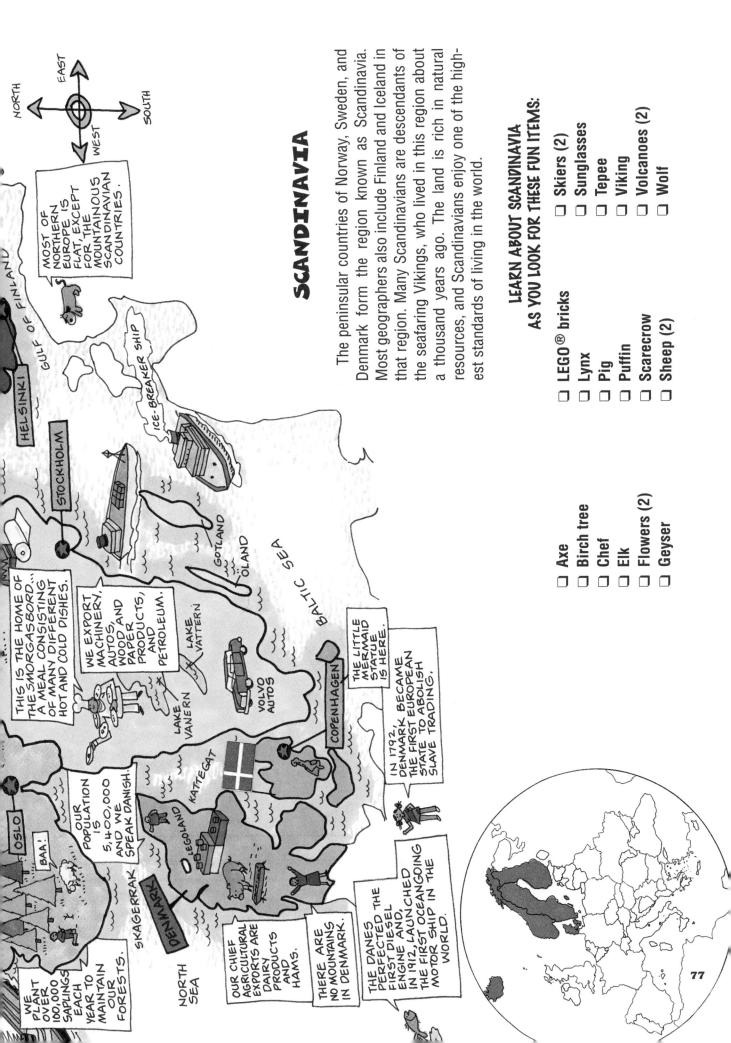

SCANDINAVIA

The peninsular countries of Norway, Sweden, and Denmark form the region known as Scandinavia. Most geographers also include Finland and Iceland in that region. Many Scandinavians are descendants of the seafaring Vikings, who lived in this region about a thousand years ago. The land is rich in natural resources, and Scandinavians enjoy one of the highest standards of living in the world.

LEARN ABOUT SCANDINAVIA
AS YOU LOOK FOR THESE FUN ITEMS:

☐ LEGO® bricks
☐ Lynx
☐ Pig
☐ Puffin
☐ Scarecrow
☐ Sheep (2)

☐ Skiers (2)
☐ Sunglasses
☐ Tepee
☐ Viking
☐ Volcanoes (2)
☐ Wolf

☐ Axe
☐ Birch tree
☐ Chef
☐ Elk
☐ Flowers (2)
☐ Geyser

NORTH
EAST
WEST
SOUTH

GULF OF FINLAND

MOST OF NORTHERN EUROPE IS FLAT, EXCEPT FOR THE MOUNTAINOUS SCANDINAVIAN COUNTRIES.

HELSINKI

ICE-BREAKER SHIP

STOCKHOLM

GOTLAND

OLAND

BALTIC SEA

THIS IS THE HOME OF THE SMORGASBORD... A MEAL CONSISTING OF MANY DIFFERENT HOT AND COLD DISHES.

WE EXPORT MACHINERY, AUTOS, WOOD AND PAPER PRODUCTS, AND PETROLEUM.

LAKE VATTERN

LAKE VANERN

VOLVO AUTOS

COPENHAGEN

THE LITTLE MERMAID STATUE IS HERE.

IN 1792, DENMARK BECAME THE FIRST EUROPEAN STATE TO ABOLISH SLAVE TRADING.

KATTEGAT

LEGOLAND

SKAGERRAK

DENMARK

OUR CHIEF AGRICULTURAL EXPORTS ARE DAIRY PRODUCTS AND HAMS.

THERE ARE NO MOUNTAINS IN DENMARK.

THE DANES PERFECTED THE FIRST DIESEL ENGINE AND, IN 1912, LAUNCHED THE FIRST OCEANGOING MOTOR SHIP IN THE WORLD.

NORTH SEA

OUR POPULATION IS 5,400,000 AND WE SPEAK DANISH.

OSLO

BAA!

WE PLANT OVER 100,000 SAPLINGS EACH YEAR TO MAINTAIN OUR FORESTS.

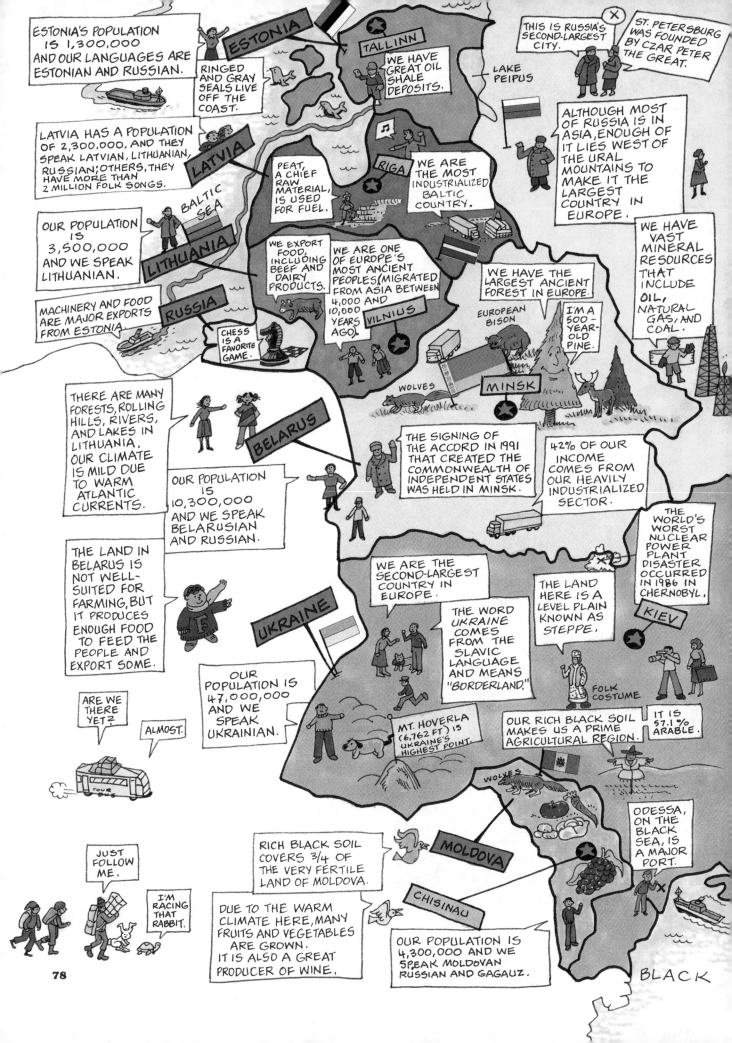

ESTONIA'S POPULATION IS 1,300,000 AND OUR LANGUAGES ARE ESTONIAN AND RUSSIAN.

RINGED AND GRAY SEALS LIVE OFF THE COAST.

ESTONIA

TALLINN

WE HAVE GREAT OIL SHALE DEPOSITS.

LAKE PEIPUS

THIS IS RUSSIA'S SECOND-LARGEST CITY.

ST. PETERSBURG WAS FOUNDED BY CZAR PETER THE GREAT.

LATVIA HAS A POPULATION OF 2,300,000, AND THEY SPEAK LATVIAN, LITHUANIAN, RUSSIAN; OTHERS, THEY HAVE MORE THAN 2 MILLION FOLK SONGS.

LATVIA

BALTIC SEA

PEAT, A CHIEF RAW MATERIAL, IS USED FOR FUEL.

RIGA

WE ARE THE MOST INDUSTRIALIZED BALTIC COUNTRY.

ALTHOUGH MOST OF RUSSIA IS IN ASIA, ENOUGH OF IT LIES WEST OF THE URAL MOUNTAINS TO MAKE IT THE LARGEST COUNTRY IN EUROPE.

OUR POPULATION IS 3,500,000 AND WE SPEAK LITHUANIAN.

LITHUANIA

WE EXPORT FOOD, INCLUDING BEEF AND DAIRY PRODUCTS.

WE ARE ONE OF EUROPE'S MOST ANCIENT PEOPLES (MIGRATED FROM ASIA BETWEEN 4,000 AND 10,000 YEARS AGO).

VILNIUS

WE HAVE THE LARGEST ANCIENT FOREST IN EUROPE.

EUROPEAN BISON

I'M A 500-YEAR-OLD PINE.

WE HAVE VAST MINERAL RESOURCES THAT INCLUDE OIL, NATURAL GAS, AND COAL.

MACHINERY AND FOOD ARE MAJOR EXPORTS FROM ESTONIA.

RUSSIA

CHESS IS A FAVORITE GAME.

WOLVES

MINSK

THERE ARE MANY FORESTS, ROLLING HILLS, RIVERS, AND LAKES IN LITHUANIA. OUR CLIMATE IS MILD DUE TO WARM ATLANTIC CURRENTS.

BELARUS

OUR POPULATION IS 10,300,000 AND WE SPEAK BELARUSIAN AND RUSSIAN.

THE SIGNING OF THE ACCORD IN 1991 THAT CREATED THE COMMONWEALTH OF INDEPENDENT STATES WAS HELD IN MINSK.

42% OF OUR INCOME COMES FROM OUR HEAVILY INDUSTRIALIZED SECTOR.

THE WORLD'S WORST NUCLEAR POWER PLANT DISASTER OCCURRED IN 1986 IN CHERNOBYL.

THE LAND IN BELARUS IS NOT WELL-SUITED FOR FARMING, BUT IT PRODUCES ENOUGH FOOD TO FEED THE PEOPLE AND EXPORT SOME.

UKRAINE

WE ARE THE SECOND-LARGEST COUNTRY IN EUROPE.

THE WORD UKRAINE COMES FROM THE SLAVIC LANGUAGE AND MEANS "BORDERLAND."

THE LAND HERE IS A LEVEL PLAIN KNOWN AS STEPPE.

KIEV

ARE WE THERE YET?

ALMOST.

OUR POPULATION IS 47,000,000 AND WE SPEAK UKRAINIAN.

MT. HOVERLA (6,762 FT) IS UKRAINE'S HIGHEST POINT.

OUR RICH BLACK SOIL MAKES US A PRIME AGRICULTURAL REGION.

IT IS 57.1% ARABLE.

FOLK COSTUME

JUST FOLLOW ME.

I'M RACING THAT RABBIT.

WOLVES

ODESSA, ON THE BLACK SEA, IS A MAJOR PORT.

RICH BLACK SOIL COVERS 3/4 OF THE VERY FERTILE LAND OF MOLDOVA.

MOLDOVA

CHISINAU

DUE TO THE WARM CLIMATE HERE, MANY FRUITS AND VEGETABLES ARE GROWN. IT IS ALSO A GREAT PRODUCER OF WINE.

OUR POPULATION IS 4,300,000 AND WE SPEAK MOLDOVAN RUSSIAN AND GAGAUZ.

BLACK

78

THE BALTIC NATIONS AND EUROPEAN RUSSIA

Before 1991, the countries in this region were part of the vast Soviet Union—also called the Union of Soviet Socialist Republics, or U.S.S.R. In 1991, that vast country broke apart, and now Estonia, Latvia, Lithuania, Belarus, Ukraine, and Moldova are independent countries. They are called "Baltic nations" because they were in the part of the Soviet Union that lay west of Russia and on or near the Baltic Sea.

Most of Russia is in Asia, but the part west of the Ural Mountains—which includes the capital city—is part of Europe.

LEARN ABOUT THE BALTIC NATIONS AND EUROPEAN RUSSIA AS YOU LOOK FOR THESE FUN ITEMS:

- ❏ Ballet dancers
- ❏ Bus
- ❏ Camera
- ❏ Chess piece
- ❏ Duck
- ❏ Elk
- ❏ European bison
- ❏ Frame
- ❏ Mouse
- ❏ Rabbit
- ❏ Scarecrow
- ❏ Seals (2)
- ❏ Ships (3)
- ❏ Shovel
- ❏ Statue
- ❏ Trucks (3)
- ❏ Turtle
- ❏ Wolves (2)

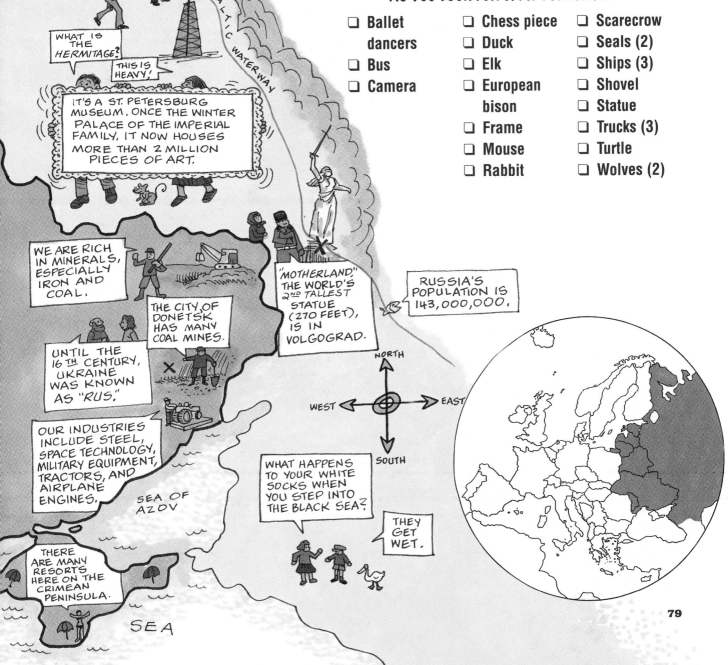

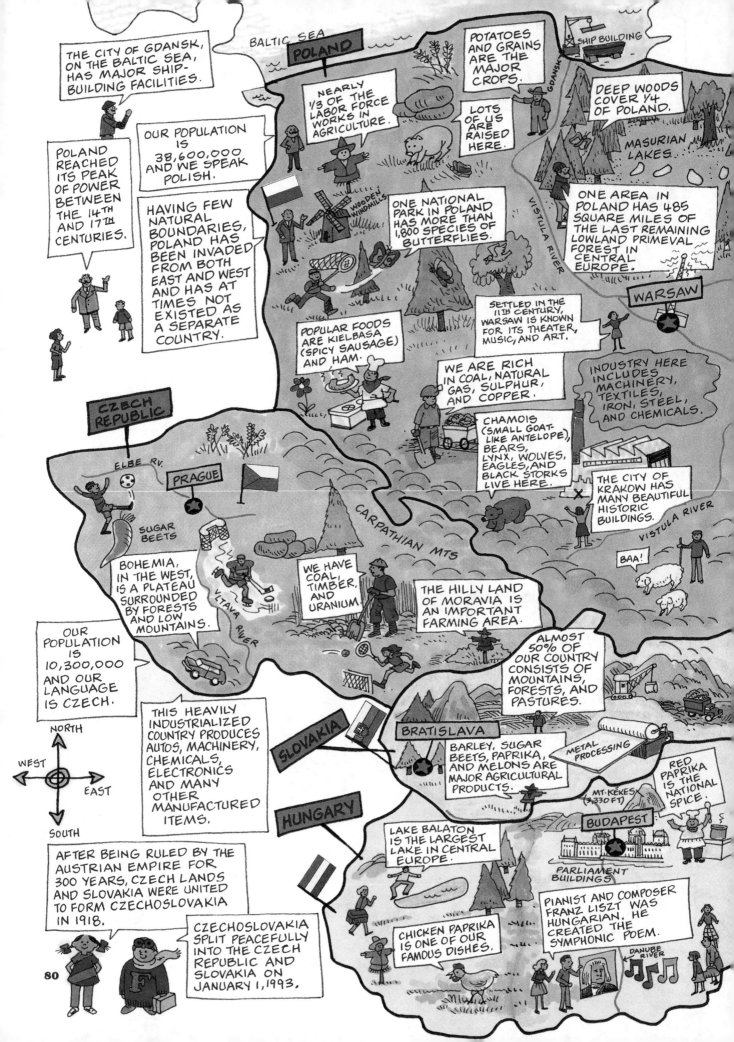

BALTIC SEA

POLAND

THE CITY OF GDANSK, ON THE BALTIC SEA, HAS MAJOR SHIP-BUILDING FACILITIES.

SHIP BUILDING

POTATOES AND GRAINS ARE THE MAJOR CROPS.

NEARLY 1/3 OF THE LABOR FORCE WORKS IN AGRICULTURE.

LOTS OF US ARE RAISED HERE.

DEEP WOODS COVER 1/4 OF POLAND.

MASURIAN LAKES

POLAND REACHED ITS PEAK OF POWER BETWEEN THE 14TH AND 17TH CENTURIES.

OUR POPULATION IS 38,600,000 AND WE SPEAK POLISH.

HAVING FEW NATURAL BOUNDARIES, POLAND HAS BEEN INVADED FROM BOTH EAST AND WEST AND HAS AT TIMES NOT EXISTED AS A SEPARATE COUNTRY.

WOODEN WINDMILLS

ONE NATIONAL PARK IN POLAND HAS MORE THAN 1,800 SPECIES OF BUTTERFLIES.

VISTULA RIVER

ONE AREA IN POLAND HAS 485 SQUARE MILES OF THE LAST REMAINING LOWLAND PRIMEVAL FOREST IN CENTRAL EUROPE.

WARSAW

SETTLED IN THE 11TH CENTURY, WARSAW IS KNOWN FOR ITS THEATER, MUSIC, AND ART.

POPULAR FOODS ARE KIELBASA (SPICY SAUSAGE) AND HAM.

WE ARE RICH IN COAL, NATURAL GAS, SULPHUR, AND COPPER.

INDUSTRY HERE INCLUDES MACHINERY, TEXTILES, IRON, STEEL, AND CHEMICALS.

CZECH REPUBLIC

ELBE RV.

PRAGUE

CHAMOIS (SMALL GOAT-LIKE ANTELOPE), BEARS, LYNX, WOLVES, EAGLES, AND BLACK STORKS LIVE HERE.

THE CITY OF KRAKOW HAS MANY BEAUTIFUL HISTORIC BUILDINGS.

VISTULA RIVER

SUGAR BEETS

CARPATHIAN MTS

BAA!

BOHEMIA, IN THE WEST, IS A PLATEAU SURROUNDED BY FORESTS AND LOW MOUNTAINS.

VLTAVA RIVER

WE HAVE COAL, TIMBER, AND URANIUM.

THE HILLY LAND OF MORAVIA IS AN IMPORTANT FARMING AREA.

OUR POPULATION IS 10,300,000 AND OUR LANGUAGE IS CZECH.

ALMOST 50% OF OUR COUNTRY CONSISTS OF MOUNTAINS, FORESTS, AND PASTURES.

NORTH
WEST
EAST
SOUTH

THIS HEAVILY INDUSTRIALIZED COUNTRY PRODUCES AUTOS, MACHINERY, CHEMICALS, ELECTRONICS AND MANY OTHER MANUFACTURED ITEMS.

SLOVAKIA

BRATISLAVA

METAL PROCESSING

BARLEY, SUGAR BEETS, PAPRIKA, AND MELONS ARE MAJOR AGRICULTURAL PRODUCTS.

RED PAPRIKA IS THE NATIONAL SPICE.

HUNGARY

MT. KÉKES (3,330 FT)

BUDAPEST

LAKE BALATON IS THE LARGEST LAKE IN CENTRAL EUROPE.

AFTER BEING RULED BY THE AUSTRIAN EMPIRE FOR 300 YEARS, CZECH LANDS AND SLOVAKIA WERE UNITED TO FORM CZECHOSLOVAKIA IN 1918.

CZECHOSLOVAKIA SPLIT PEACEFULLY INTO THE CZECH REPUBLIC AND SLOVAKIA ON JANUARY 1, 1993.

PARLIAMENT BUILDINGS

CHICKEN PAPRIKA IS ONE OF OUR FAMOUS DISHES.

PIANIST AND COMPOSER FRANZ LISZT WAS HUNGARIAN. HE CREATED THE SYMPHONIC POEM.

DANUBE RIVER

POLAND, CZECH REPUBLIC, SLOVAKIA, AND HUNGARY

When World War II ended in 1945, many countries in Eastern Europe came under the control of the Soviet Union. When the Soviet Union broke apart in 1991, the people in Poland, Czechoslovakia, and Hungary once again took charge of their own governments. In 1993, Czechoslovakia split into two independent countries, the Czech Republic and Slovakia.

LEARN ABOUT POLAND, CZECH REPUBLC, SLOVAKIA, AND HUNGARY AS YOU LOOK FOR THESE FUN ITEMS:

- ❏ Barn
- ❏ Bear
- ❏ Bird
- ❏ European bison
- ❏ Butterflies (4)
- ❏ Carrot
- ❏ Cooks (3)
- ❏ Flower
- ❏ Hockey player
- ❏ Musical notes
- ❏ Pigs (2)
- ❏ Radio tower
- ❏ Sausage
- ❏ Scarecrows (5)
- ❏ Sheep
- ❏ Tennis ball
- ❏ Tourists
- ❏ Truck
- ❏ Windmill
- ❏ Woolly mammoth

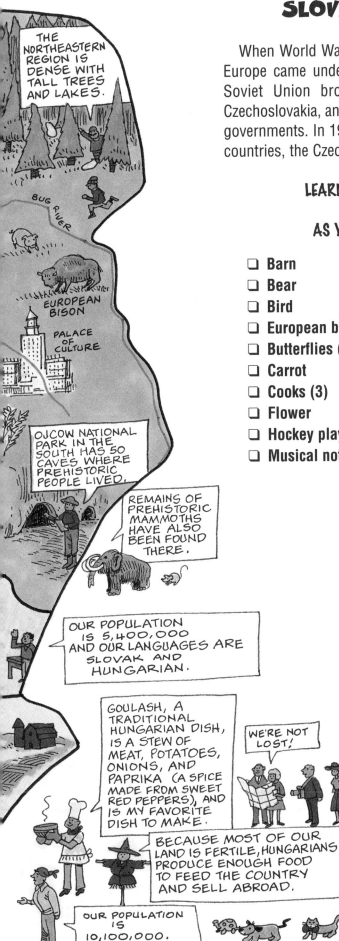

THE NORTHEASTERN REGION IS DENSE WITH TALL TREES AND LAKES.

BUG RIVER

EUROPEAN BISON

PALACE OF CULTURE

OJCOW NATIONAL PARK IN THE SOUTH HAS 50 CAVES WHERE PREHISTORIC PEOPLE LIVED.

REMAINS OF PREHISTORIC MAMMOTHS HAVE ALSO BEEN FOUND THERE.

OUR POPULATION IS 5,400,000 AND OUR LANGUAGES ARE SLOVAK AND HUNGARIAN.

GOULASH, A TRADITIONAL HUNGARIAN DISH, IS A STEW OF MEAT, POTATOES, ONIONS, AND PAPRIKA (A SPICE MADE FROM SWEET RED PEPPERS), AND IS MY FAVORITE DISH TO MAKE.

WE'RE NOT LOST!

BECAUSE MOST OF OUR LAND IS FERTILE, HUNGARIANS PRODUCE ENOUGH FOOD TO FEED THE COUNTRY AND SELL ABROAD.

OUR POPULATION IS 10,100,000.

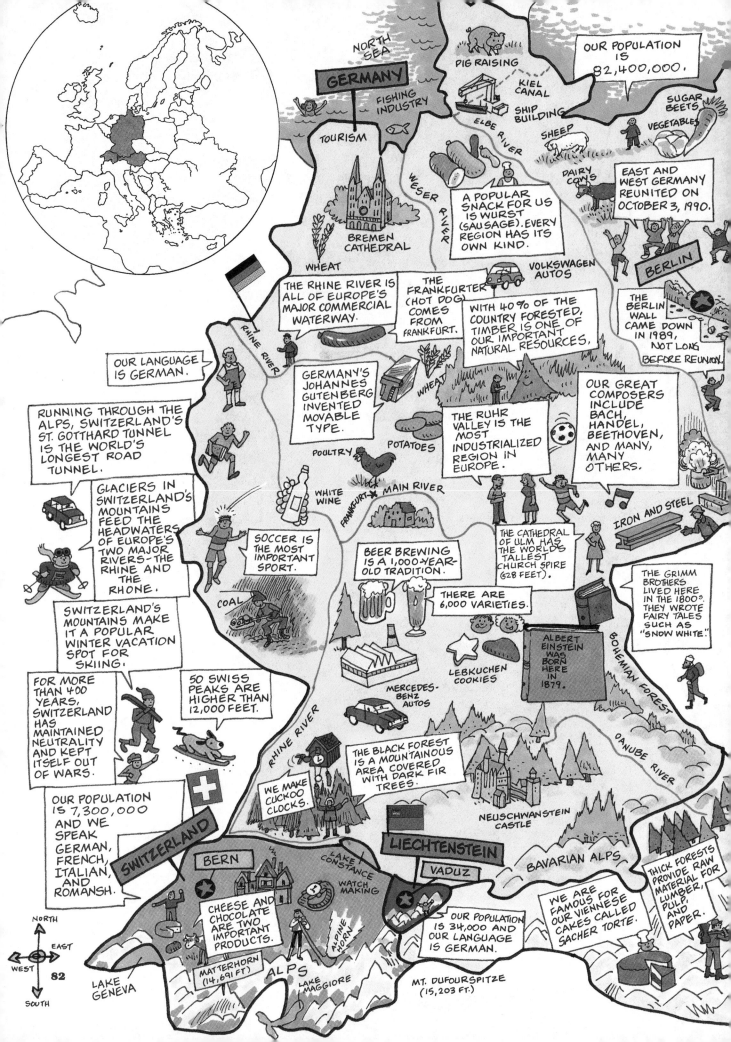

NORTH SEA

PIG RAISING

GERMANY

FISHING INDUSTRY

KIEL CANAL

SHIP BUILDING

OUR POPULATION IS 82,400,000.

ELBE RIVER

SHEEP

SUGAR BEETS

VEGETABLES

TOURISM

WESER RIVER

DAIRY COWS

EAST AND WEST GERMANY REUNITED ON OCTOBER 3, 1990.

BREMEN CATHEDRAL

A POPULAR SNACK FOR US IS WURST (SAUSAGE). EVERY REGION HAS ITS OWN KIND.

WHEAT

VOLKSWAGEN AUTOS

BERLIN

THE RHINE RIVER IS ALL OF EUROPE'S MAJOR COMMERCIAL WATERWAY.

THE FRANKFURTER (HOT DOG) COMES FROM FRANKFURT.

WITH 40% OF THE COUNTRY FORESTED, TIMBER IS ONE OF OUR IMPORTANT NATURAL RESOURCES.

THE BERLIN WALL CAME DOWN IN 1989, NOT LONG BEFORE REUNION.

OUR LANGUAGE IS GERMAN.

RHINE RIVER

GERMANY'S JOHANNES GUTENBERG INVENTED MOVABLE TYPE.

WHEAT

OUR GREAT COMPOSERS INCLUDE BACH, HANDEL, BEETHOVEN, AND MANY, MANY OTHERS.

RUNNING THROUGH THE ALPS, SWITZERLAND'S ST. GOTTHARD TUNNEL IS THE WORLD'S LONGEST ROAD TUNNEL.

POULTRY

POTATOES

THE RUHR VALLEY IS THE MOST INDUSTRIALIZED REGION IN EUROPE.

GLACIERS IN SWITZERLAND'S MOUNTAINS FEED THE HEADWATERS OF EUROPE'S TWO MAJOR RIVERS—THE RHINE AND THE RHONE.

WHITE WINE

MAIN RIVER

FRANKFURT

SOCCER IS THE MOST IMPORTANT SPORT.

BEER BREWING IS A 1,000-YEAR-OLD TRADITION.

THE CATHEDRAL OF ULM HAS THE WORLD'S TALLEST CHURCH SPIRE (528 FEET).

IRON AND STEEL

SWITZERLAND'S MOUNTAINS MAKE IT A POPULAR WINTER VACATION SPOT FOR SKIING.

COAL

THERE ARE 6,000 VARIETIES.

THE GRIMM BROTHERS LIVED HERE IN THE 1800s. THEY WROTE FAIRY TALES SUCH AS "SNOW WHITE."

FOR MORE THAN 400 YEARS, SWITZERLAND HAS MAINTAINED NEUTRALITY AND KEPT ITSELF OUT OF WARS.

50 SWISS PEAKS ARE HIGHER THAN 12,000 FEET.

MERCEDES-BENZ AUTOS

LEBKUCHEN COOKIES

ALBERT EINSTEIN WAS BORN HERE IN 1879.

BOHEMIAN FOREST

OUR POPULATION IS 7,300,000 AND WE SPEAK GERMAN, FRENCH, ITALIAN, AND ROMANSH.

RHINE RIVER

WE MAKE CUCKOO CLOCKS.

THE BLACK FOREST IS A MOUNTAINOUS AREA COVERED WITH DARK FIR TREES.

DANUBE RIVER

NEUSCHWANSTEIN CASTLE

SWITZERLAND

BERN

LAKE CONSTANCE

WATCH MAKING

LIECHTENSTEIN

VADUZ

BAVARIAN ALPS

THICK FORESTS PROVIDE RAW MATERIAL FOR LUMBER, PULP, AND PAPER.

CHEESE AND CHOCOLATE ARE TWO IMPORTANT PRODUCTS.

ALPINE HORN

WE ARE FAMOUS FOR OUR VIENNESE CAKES CALLED SACHER TORTE.

OUR POPULATION IS 34,000 AND OUR LANGUAGE IS GERMAN.

MATTERHORN (14,691 FT)

ALPS

LAKE GENEVA

LAKE MAGGIORE

MT. DUFOURSPITZE (15,203 FT.)

GERMANY, SWITZERLAND, LIECHTENSTEIN, AND AUSTRIA

The countries of Germany, Switzerland, Liechtenstein, and Austria lie in an area sometimes known as central Europe. From north to south, this region's landscape changes from marshy plains to snowcapped moutains. It is crossed by two of Europe's longest rivers—the Rhine and the Danube—and by the Alps, the famous mountain range that is the longest and highest mountain range in western Europe.

LEARN ABOUT GERMANY, SWITZERLAND, LIECHTENSTEIN, AND AUSTRIA AS YOU LOOK FOR THESE FUN ITEMS:

- ❏ Alpine horn blower
- ❏ Automobiles (3)
- ❏ Axe
- ❏ Berlin Wall
- ❏ Books (3)
- ❏ Cake
- ❏ Carrot

- ❏ Chicken
- ❏ Coal miner
- ❏ Cookies
- ❏ Cows (2)
- ❏ Cuckoo clock
- ❏ Dogs (2)
- ❏ Great white heron

- ❏ Horse
- ❏ Hot dogs
- ❏ Pigs (2)
- ❏ Soccer ball
- ❏ Telescope
- ❏ Tuba
- ❏ Watch

TEXTILES

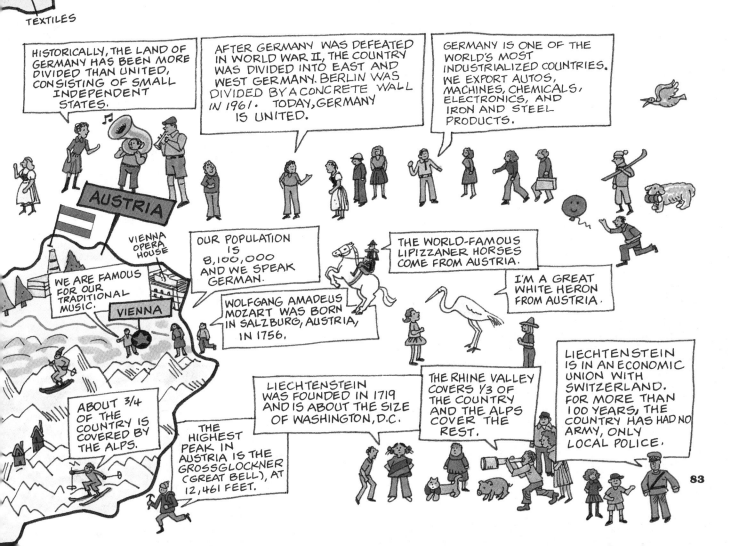

HISTORICALLY, THE LAND OF GERMANY HAS BEEN MORE DIVIDED THAN UNITED, CONSISTING OF SMALL INDEPENDENT STATES.

AFTER GERMANY WAS DEFEATED IN WORLD WAR II, THE COUNTRY WAS DIVIDED INTO EAST AND WEST GERMANY. BERLIN WAS DIVIDED BY A CONCRETE WALL IN 1961. TODAY, GERMANY IS UNITED.

GERMANY IS ONE OF THE WORLD'S MOST INDUSTRIALIZED COUNTRIES. WE EXPORT AUTOS, MACHINES, CHEMICALS, ELECTRONICS, AND IRON AND STEEL PRODUCTS.

AUSTRIA

VIENNA OPERA HOUSE

WE ARE FAMOUS FOR OUR TRADITIONAL MUSIC.

VIENNA

OUR POPULATION IS 8,100,000 AND WE SPEAK GERMAN.

THE WORLD-FAMOUS LIPIZZANER HORSES COME FROM AUSTRIA.

I'M A GREAT WHITE HERON FROM AUSTRIA.

WOLFGANG AMADEUS MOZART WAS BORN IN SALZBURG, AUSTRIA, IN 1756.

ABOUT 3/4 OF THE COUNTRY IS COVERED BY THE ALPS.

LIECHTENSTEIN WAS FOUNDED IN 1719 AND IS ABOUT THE SIZE OF WASHINGTON, D.C.

THE RHINE VALLEY COVERS 1/3 OF THE COUNTRY AND THE ALPS COVER THE REST.

LIECHTENSTEIN IS IN AN ECONOMIC UNION WITH SWITZERLAND. FOR MORE THAN 100 YEARS, THE COUNTRY HAS HAD NO ARMY, ONLY LOCAL POLICE.

THE HIGHEST PEAK IN AUSTRIA IS THE GROSSGLOCKNER (GREAT BELL), AT 12,461 FEET.

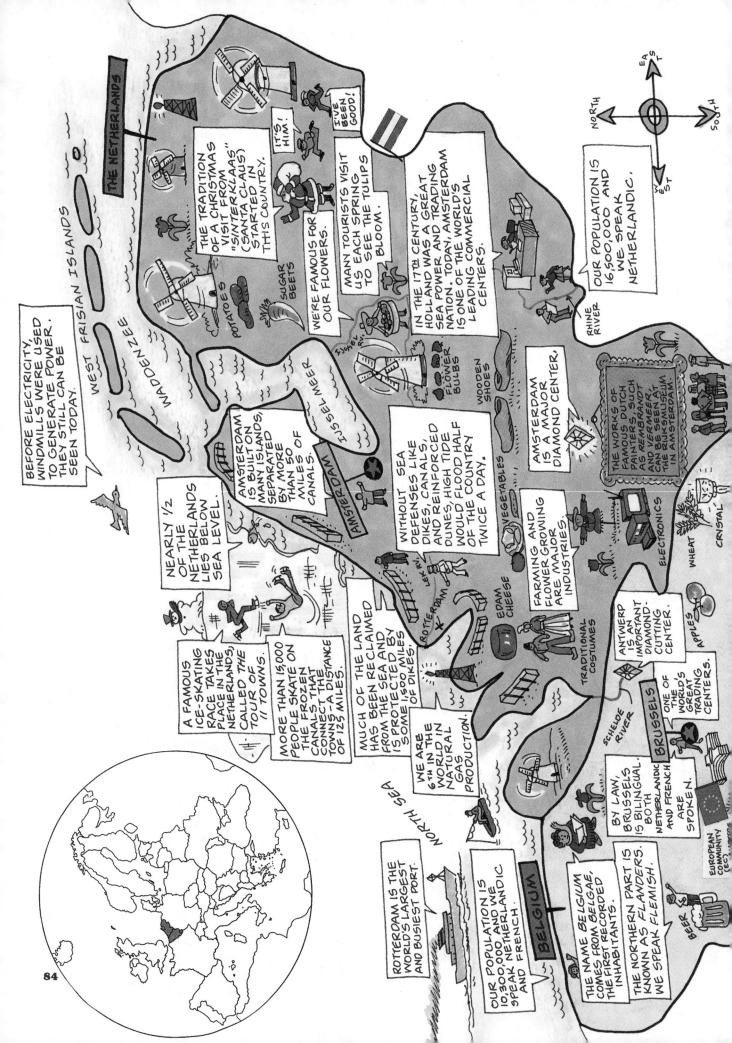

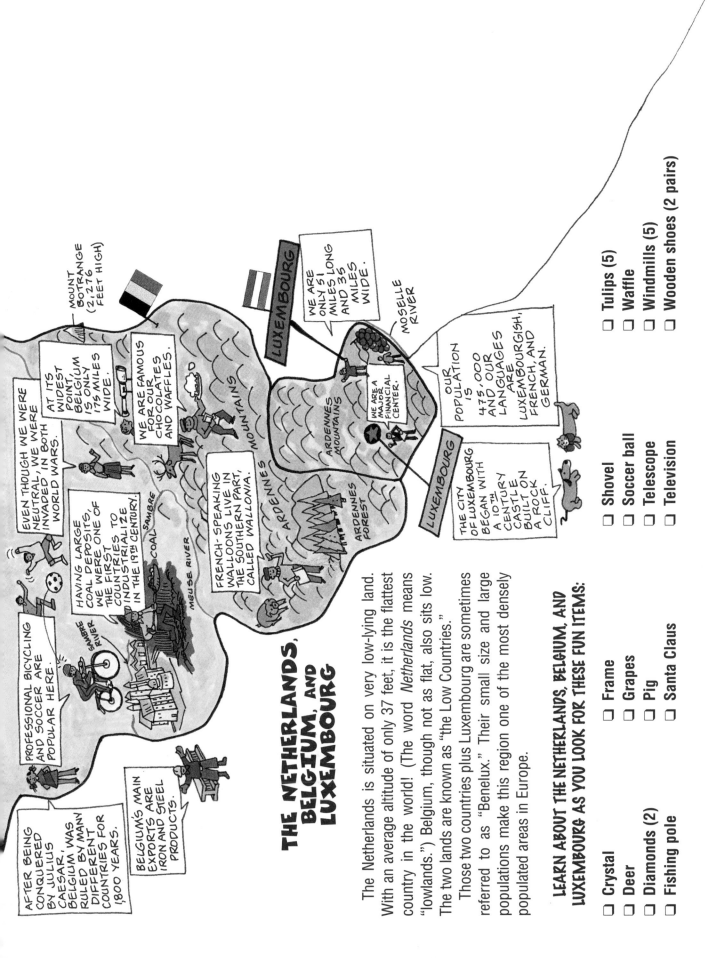

THE NETHERLANDS, BELGIUM, AND LUXEMBOURG

The Netherlands is situated on very low-lying land. With an average altitude of only 37 feet, it is the flattest country in the world! (The word *Netherlands* means "lowlands.") Belgium, though not as flat, also sits low. The two lands are known as "the Low Countries."

Those two countries plus Luxembourg are sometimes referred to as "Benelux." Their small size and large populations make this region one of the most densely populated areas in Europe.

LEARN ABOUT THE NETHERLANDS, BELGIUM, AND LUXEMBOURG AS YOU LOOK FOR THESE FUN ITEMS:

- ☐ Crystal
- ☐ Deer
- ☐ Diamonds (2)
- ☐ Fishing pole
- ☐ Frame
- ☐ Grapes
- ☐ Pig
- ☐ Santa Claus
- ☐ Shovel
- ☐ Soccer ball
- ☐ Telescope
- ☐ Television
- ☐ Tulips (5)
- ☐ Waffle
- ☐ Windmills (5)
- ☐ Wooden shoes (2 pairs)

FRANCE AND MONACO

France is one of the oldest countries in Europe. It also is one of the world's leading countries in terms of culture, historic and political influence, industry, and agriculture. The capital and cultural center is the city of Paris, nicknamed "the City of Light."

At France's southeastern corner lies Monaco, one of the world's smallest nations. (*Monaco* is also the name of its capital city.)

LEARN ABOUT FRANCE AND MONACO AS YOU LOOK FOR THESE FUN ITEMS:

- ❑ Apples (2)
- ❑ Artichoke
- ❑ Artist
- ❑ Automobile
- ❑ Chef
- ❑ Cyclist
- ❑ Dice
- ❑ Dijon mustard
- ❑ Eels
- ❑ Eiffel Tower
- ❑ Geese (2)
- ❑ Mouse
- ❑ Musician
- ❑ Napoleon
- ❑ Paper airplane
- ❑ Perfume bottle
- ❑ Pig
- ❑ Red balloon
- ❑ Skier
- ❑ Snail
- ❑ Soccer ball
- ❑ Umbrellas (2)
- ❑ Walnuts

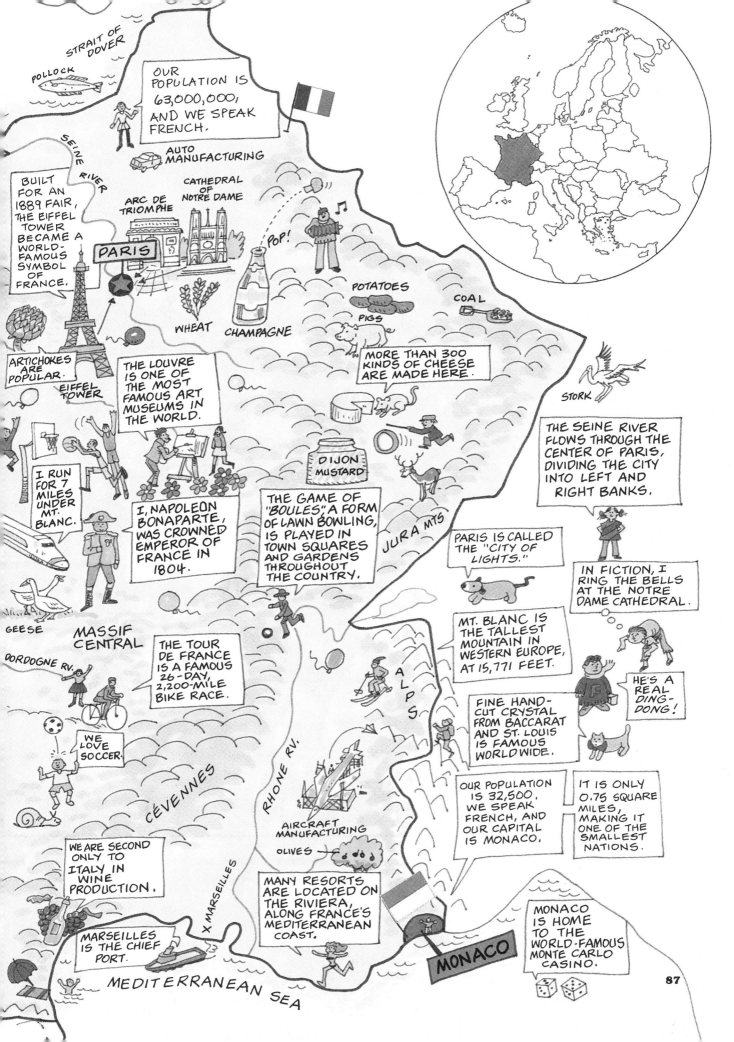

STRAIT OF DOVER

POLLOCK

OUR POPULATION IS 63,000,000, AND WE SPEAK FRENCH.

AUTO MANUFACTURING

SEINE RIVER

BUILT FOR AN 1889 FAIR, THE EIFFEL TOWER BECAME A WORLD-FAMOUS SYMBOL OF FRANCE.

ARC DE TRIOMPHE

CATHEDRAL OF NOTRE DAME

PARIS

POP!

POTATOES

PIGS

COAL

WHEAT

CHAMPAGNE

MORE THAN 300 KINDS OF CHEESE ARE MADE HERE.

ARTICHOKES ARE POPULAR.

EIFFEL TOWER

STORK

THE LOUVRE IS ONE OF THE MOST FAMOUS ART MUSEUMS IN THE WORLD.

THE SEINE RIVER FLOWS THROUGH THE CENTER OF PARIS, DIVIDING THE CITY INTO LEFT AND RIGHT BANKS.

I RUN FOR 7 MILES UNDER MT. BLANC.

DIJON MUSTARD

I, NAPOLEON BONAPARTE, WAS CROWNED EMPEROR OF FRANCE IN 1804.

THE GAME OF "BOULES," A FORM OF LAWN BOWLING, IS PLAYED IN TOWN SQUARES AND GARDENS THROUGHOUT THE COUNTRY.

JURA MTS

PARIS IS CALLED THE "CITY OF LIGHTS."

IN FICTION, I RING THE BELLS AT THE NOTRE DAME CATHEDRAL.

GEESE

MASSIF CENTRAL

MT. BLANC IS THE TALLEST MOUNTAIN IN WESTERN EUROPE, AT 15,771 FEET.

HE'S A REAL DING-DONG!

DORDOGNE RV.

THE TOUR DE FRANCE IS A FAMOUS 26-DAY, 2,200-MILE BIKE RACE.

ALPS

WE LOVE SOCCER.

FINE HAND-CUT CRYSTAL FROM BACCARAT AND ST. LOUIS IS FAMOUS WORLDWIDE.

CÉVENNES

RHONE RV.

OUR POPULATION IS 32,500. WE SPEAK FRENCH, AND OUR CAPITAL IS MONACO.

IT IS ONLY 0.75 SQUARE MILES, MAKING IT ONE OF THE SMALLEST NATIONS.

AIRCRAFT MANUFACTURING

OLIVES

WE ARE SECOND ONLY TO ITALY IN WINE PRODUCTION.

X MARSEILLES

MANY RESORTS ARE LOCATED ON THE RIVIERA, ALONG FRANCE'S MEDITERRANEAN COAST.

MONACO IS HOME TO THE WORLD-FAMOUS MONTE CARLO CASINO.

MARSEILLES IS THE CHIEF PORT.

MONACO

MEDITERRANEAN SEA

THE IBERIAN PENINSULA

Spain, Portugal, and Andorra share a piece of land called the Iberian Peninsula. (A *peninsula* is a land area with water on all sides except for a neck of land connected to a larger landmass.) Spain and Portugal have long seafaring histories. Their explorers and settlers once ruled empires in Africa, Asia, North America, and South America. Tiny Andorra, tucked into an area of the Pyrenees Mountains, is landlocked.

Today, fishing, farming, and tourism are major industries in Spain and Portugal. More than 60 million tourists each year visit their historical cities and sun-drenched beaches.

LEARN ABOUT THE IBERIAN PENINSULA AS YOU LOOK FOR THESE FUN ITEMS:

☐ **Anchovies**
☐ **Bottles (5)**
☐ **Brown bear**
☐ **Bulls (3)**
☐ **Cheese**
☐ **Cork**
☐ **Guitar**
☐ **Ibex**
☐ **Olive tree**

☐ **Skier**
☐ **Sunflowers (4)**
☐ **Umbrellas (3)**
☐ **Windmill**
☐ **Windsurfers (3)**

WE ARE 4TH IN EUROPE IN AUTO MANUFACTURING

WHERE'S MY CAR?

I DON'T DRIVE!

PORT WINE COMES FROM THE CITY OF PORTO.

GRAIN

POTATOES

FISH PROCESSING

BULLS ARE FOUGHT ON HORSEBACK AND ARE NOT KILLED IN PORTUGAL.

SOCCER AND BULLFIGHTING ARE POPULAR HERE.

THE TAGUS RIVER DIVIDES THE COUNTRY IN TWO.

PORTUGAL

TAGUS RIVER

PORTUGAL IS THE WESTERNMOST COUNTRY IN MAINLAND EUROPE.

LISBON

20% OF THE POPULATION LIVES IN LISBON.

GUADIANA RIVER

CITRUS FRUIT

ATLANTIC OCEAN

70% OF THE WORLD'S CORK COMES FROM HERE.

AZORES (PORTUGAL)

CORK

MADEIRA (PORTUGAL)

OUR POPULATION IS 10,400,000 AND WE SPEAK PORTUGUESE.

OLIVES

GUADALQUIVIR RIVER

THE SPANISH PEOPLE HAVE MANY REGIONAL DIFFERENCES DUE TO THE SEPARATION BROUGHT ABOUT BY THE MOUNTAIN RANGES.

VASCO DE GAMA, IN 1497, WAS THE FIRST PERSON TO SAIL AROUND THE TIP OF AFRICA.

FERDINAND MAGELLAN WAS THE FIRST TO SAIL AROUND THE WORLD.

WE ARE THE THIRD LARGEST COUNTRY IN EUROPE.

SHERRY WINE

I'M LATE FOR SCHOOL.

CANARY ISLANDS (SPAIN)

NORTH

EAST

WEST

TALLEST MOUNTAIN IN SPAIN IS *PICO DE TEIDE* (12,198 FEET).

SPAIN'S NATURAL MINERAL RESOURCES INCLUDE IRON, COAL, ZINC, AND URANIUM.

STRAIT OF GIBRALTAR

GIBRALTAR (2 3/4 MILES LONG AND RISES TO 1,394 FEET)

THE AVERAGE YEARLY RAINFALL IN SPAIN IS 20 INCHES —THE LOWEST IN WESTERN EUROPE.

ALBORAN SEA

SOUTH

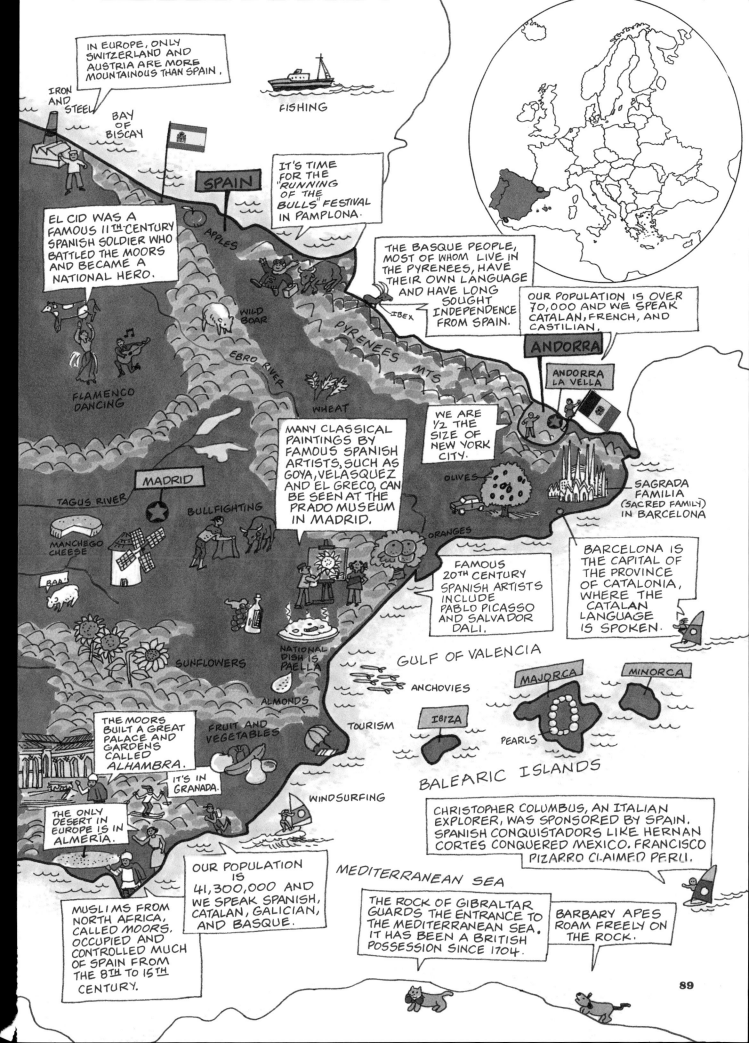

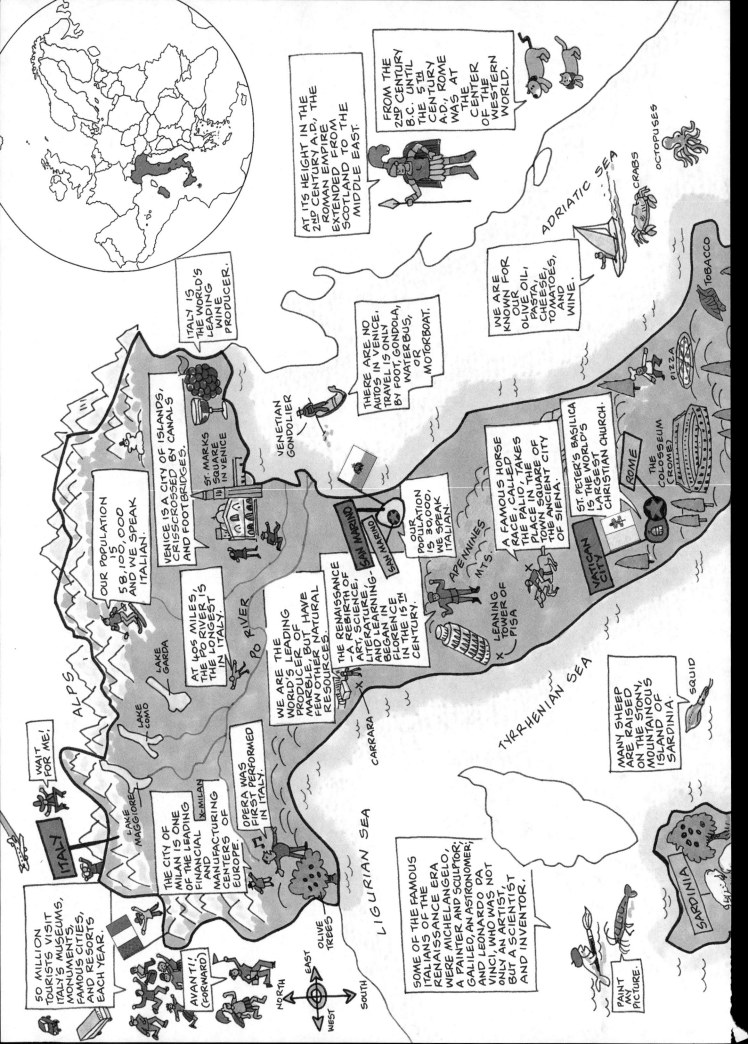

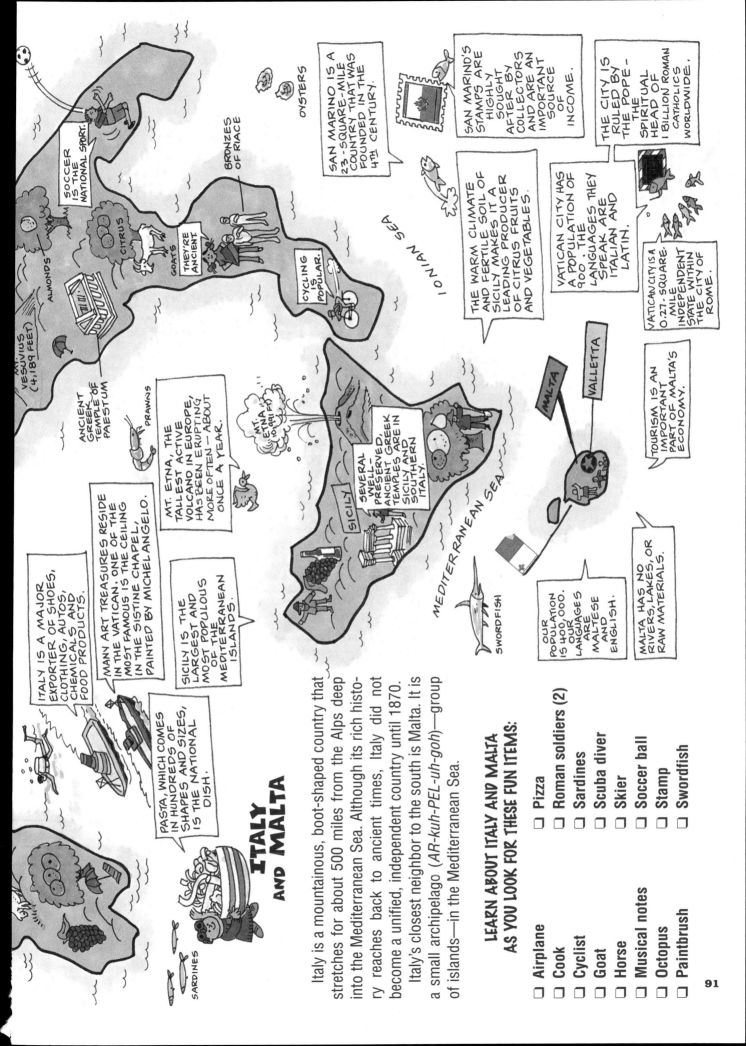

ITALY AND MALTA

Italy is a mountainous, boot-shaped country that stretches for about 500 miles deep into the Mediterranean Sea. Although its rich history reaches back to ancient times, Italy did not become a unified, independent country until 1870. Italy's closest neighbor to the south is Malta. It is a small archipelago (AR-kuh-PEL-uh-goh)—group of islands—in the Mediterranean Sea.

LEARN ABOUT ITALY AND MALTA AS YOU LOOK FOR THESE FUN ITEMS:

☐ Airplane
☐ Cook
☐ Cyclist
☐ Goat
☐ Horse
☐ Musical notes
☐ Octopus
☐ Paintbrush

☐ Pizza
☐ Roman soldiers (2)
☐ Sardines
☐ Scuba diver
☐ Skier
☐ Soccer ball
☐ Stamp
☐ Swordfish

THE BALKAN NATIONS

Much of this part of eastern Europe, known as the Balkans, was ruled by Turkey from the end of the 15th century until 1913. (The name *Balkan* comes from the Balkan Mountains of Bulgaria.) After World War I, several regions were combined to form Yugoslavia. The new country was heavily influenced by its huge neighbor, the Soviet Union. Soon after the Soviet Union broke apart in 1991, so did Yugoslavia. That land is now six independent countries: Serbia, Montenegro, Slovenia, Croatia, Bosnia and Herzegovina, and Macedonia.

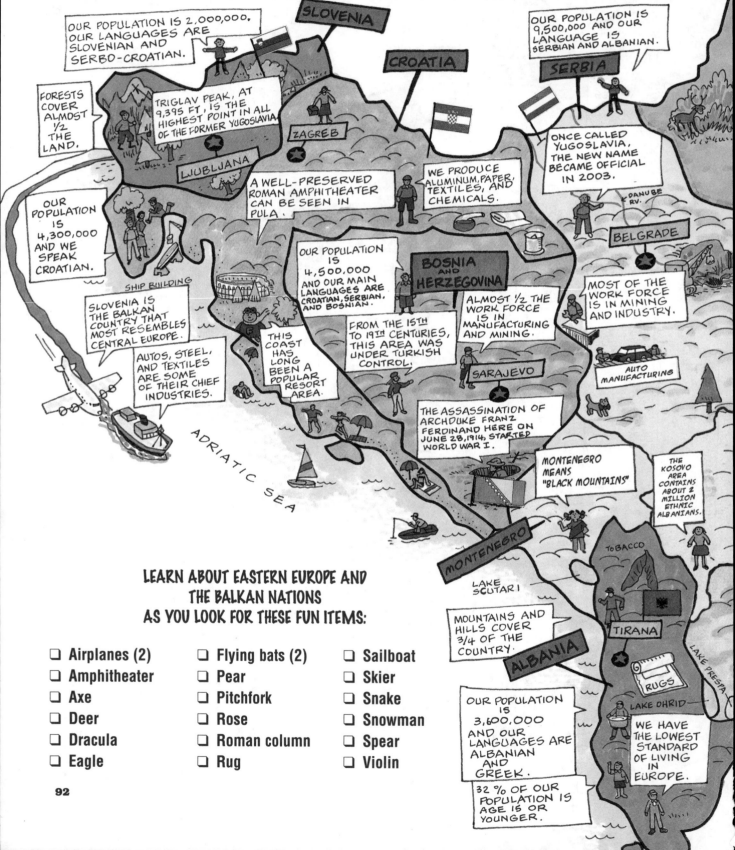

LEARN ABOUT EASTERN EUROPE AND THE BALKAN NATIONS AS YOU LOOK FOR THESE FUN ITEMS:

- ❑ Airplanes (2)
- ❑ Amphitheater
- ❑ Axe
- ❑ Deer
- ❑ Dracula
- ❑ Eagle
- ❑ Flying bats (2)
- ❑ Pear
- ❑ Pitchfork
- ❑ Rose
- ❑ Roman column
- ❑ Rug
- ❑ Sailboat
- ❑ Skier
- ❑ Snake
- ❑ Snowman
- ❑ Spear
- ❑ Violin

GREECE

The ideals of Western democracy were born in Greece about 2,500 years ago. The art, philosophy, theater, mythology, science, and architecture that flourished there formed the basis of Western civilization.

LEARN ABOUT GREECE AS YOU LOOK FOR THESE FUN ITEMS:
- ☐ Book
- ☐ Cotton
- ☐ Grapes
- ☐ Octopus
- ☐ Olympic torch bearer
- ☐ Sailboat
- ☐ Stone lion
- ☐ Telescope

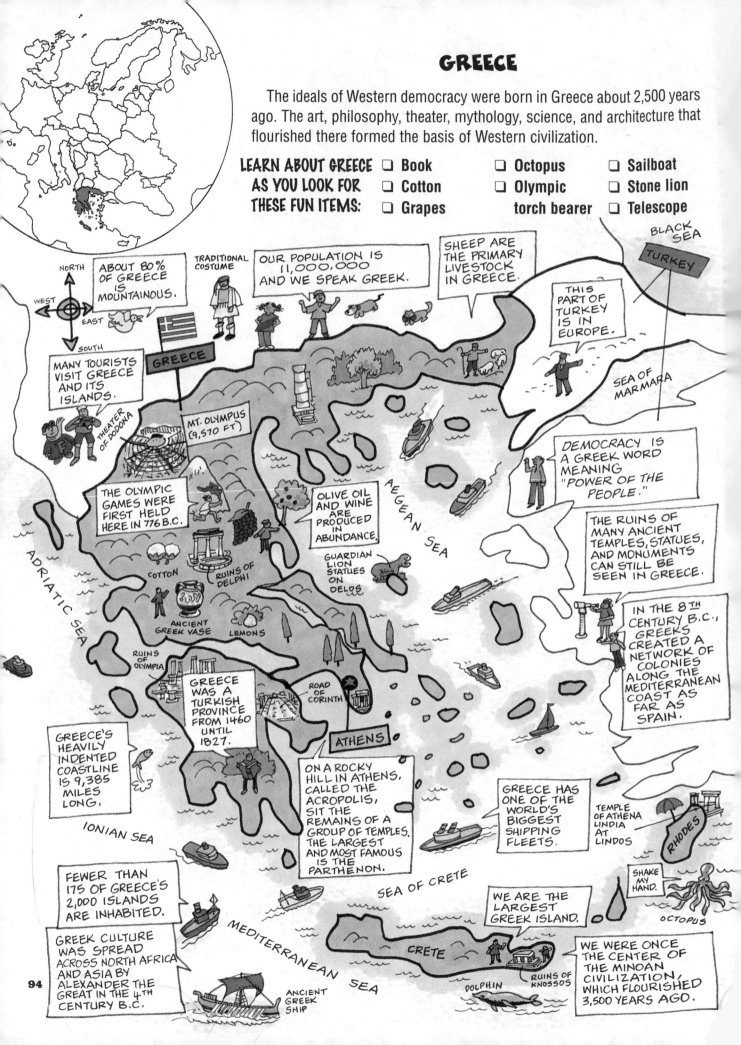

NORTH
WEST • EAST
SOUTH

ABOUT 80% OF GREECE IS MOUNTAINOUS.

TRADITIONAL COSTUME

OUR POPULATION IS 11,000,000 AND WE SPEAK GREEK.

SHEEP ARE THE PRIMARY LIVESTOCK IN GREECE.

BLACK SEA

TURKEY

THIS PART OF TURKEY IS IN EUROPE.

GREECE

MANY TOURISTS VISIT GREECE AND ITS ISLANDS.

THEATER OF DODONA

MT. OLYMPUS (9,570 FT)

SEA OF MARMARA

DEMOCRACY IS A GREEK WORD MEANING "POWER OF THE PEOPLE."

THE OLYMPIC GAMES WERE FIRST HELD HERE IN 776 B.C.

OLIVE OIL AND WINE ARE PRODUCED IN ABUNDANCE.

AEGEAN SEA

THE RUINS OF MANY ANCIENT TEMPLES, STATUES, AND MONUMENTS CAN STILL BE SEEN IN GREECE.

COTTON

RUINS OF DELPHI

GUARDIAN LION STATUES ON DELOS

IN THE 8TH CENTURY B.C., GREEKS CREATED A NETWORK OF COLONIES ALONG THE MEDITERRANEAN COAST AS FAR AS SPAIN.

ADRIATIC SEA

ANCIENT GREEK VASE

LEMONS

RUINS OF OLYMPIA

GREECE WAS A TURKISH PROVINCE FROM 1460 UNTIL 1827.

ROAD OF CORINTH

ATHENS

GREECE'S HEAVILY INDENTED COASTLINE IS 9,385 MILES LONG.

IONIAN SEA

ON A ROCKY HILL IN ATHENS, CALLED THE ACROPOLIS, SIT THE REMAINS OF A GROUP OF TEMPLES. THE LARGEST AND MOST FAMOUS IS THE PARTHENON.

GREECE HAS ONE OF THE WORLD'S BIGGEST SHIPPING FLEETS.

TEMPLE OF ATHENA LINDIA AT LINDOS

RHODES

SHAKE MY HAND.

FEWER THAN 175 OF GREECE'S 2,000 ISLANDS ARE INHABITED.

SEA OF CRETE

WE ARE THE LARGEST GREEK ISLAND.

OCTOPUS

GREEK CULTURE WAS SPREAD ACROSS NORTH AFRICA AND ASIA BY ALEXANDER THE GREAT IN THE 4TH CENTURY B.C.

MEDITERRANEAN SEA

ANCIENT GREEK SHIP

CRETE

DOLPHIN

RUINS OF KNOSSOS

WE WERE ONCE THE CENTER OF THE MINOAN CIVILIZATION, WHICH FLOURISHED 3,500 YEARS AGO.

94